AS/A-LEVEL YEAR 1

STUDENT GUIDE

WJEC/Eduqas

Biology

Basic biochemistry and cell organisation

Dan Foulder

PHILIP ALLAN FOR
HODDER
EDUCATION
AN HACHETTE UK COMPANY

Philip Allan, an imprint of Hodder Education, an Hachette UK company, Blenheim Court, George Street, Banbury, Oxfordshire OX16 5BH

Orders

Hachette UK Distribution, Hely Hutchinson Centre, Milton Road, Didcot, Oxfordshire, OX11 7HH

tel: 01235 827827

e-mail: education@hachette.co.uk

Lines are open 9.00 a.m.–5.00 p.m., Monday to Friday. You can also order through the Hodder Education website: www.hoddereducation.co.uk

© Dan Foulder 2015

ISBN 978-1-4718-4402-7

First printed 2015

Impression number 5 4

Year 2021

This guide has been written specifically to support students preparing for the WJEC/Eduqas AS and A-level Biology examinations. The content has been neither approved nor endorsed by WJEC/Eduqas and remains the sole responsibility of the author.

Cover photo: skampixelle/Fotolia; p. 66: Dr Gopal Murti/SPL; p. 73: J. C. Revy, ISM/SPL; p. 87: Pr G. Gimenez-Martin/SPL

Typeset by Integra Software Services Pvt. Ltd, Pondicherry, India

Printed and bound by CPI Group (UK) Ltd, Croydon, CR0 4YY

Hachette UK's policy is to use papers that are natural, renewable and recyclable products and made from wood grown in well-managed forests and other controlled sources. The logging and manufacturing processes are expected to conform to the environmental regulations of the country of origin.

Contents

Content Guidance

Questions & Answers

■ Getting the most from this book

Exam-style questions

Commentary on the questions

Tips on what you need to do to gain full marks, indicated by the icon ⓔ

Sample student answers

Practise the questions, then look at the student answers that follow.

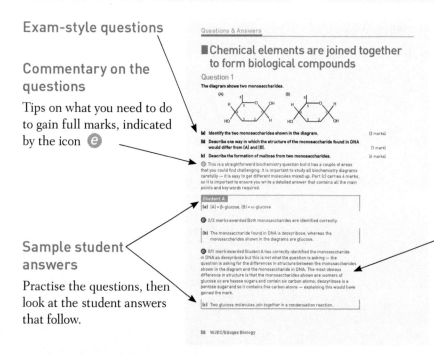

Commentary on sample student answers

Find out how many marks each answer would be awarded in the exam and then read the comments (preceded by the icon ⓔ) following each student answer.

■About this book

This guide will help you to prepare for the WJEC Biology AS/A-level Biology Unit 1 exam. The concepts in Unit 1 are fundamental and underpin the whole of A-level biology.

This guide also covers aspects of the Eduqas AS and A-level Biology:

■ Eduqas AS Biology — Component 1
■ Eduqas A-level Biology — Core Concepts and part of Component 2 (Genetic Information is copied and passed on to daughter cells)

The **Content Guidance** covers all the concepts you need to understand and facts you need to know for the exam. It also includes *exam tips* and *knowledge checks* to help you to prepare for the exam. Answers to the knowledge check questions are provided at the back of the book. At the end of each topic there is a summary of the key points covered in that topic. This is a really useful part of the book — use it when you are revising as a checklist and tick off each topic when you have revised it. You should then not look at this topic for a few days and come back to it later to test yourself and make sure that you really do know it. Each topic has specified practical work that you must complete and that you could be questioned on in the exam. The practicals are listed at the end of each topic and many of them are included in the Questions & Answers section. Mathematical skills are also an important part of A-level biology. Required skills are highlighted in exam tips and are also covered in the Questions & Answers section.

The **Questions & Answers** section contains questions on each of the topics in the specification. They are written in the same style as the questions in the Unit 1 exam so they will give you an idea of the sort of thing you will be asked to do in the exam. After each question there are answers by two students, student A and student B, followed by comments on what they have written. These comments are important because they give you an insight into the responses that the examiners are looking for in the exam. They also highlight some of the common mistakes that students make.

Revision techniques

It is important to develop effective revision and study techniques. The key to effective revision is to make it *active*. Most people cannot revise effectively by just reading through notes or a book. In order to learn, you have got to do something with the information. Here are some examples of active revision techniques — not all of them will work for everyone, so it is important that you try them and find out which techniques work for you.

Consolidate your notes

This means taking information from your notes and this book and presenting it in a different format. This can be as simple as just writing out the key points of a particular topic. One effective consolidation technique involves taking some information and turning it into a table or diagram. More creative consolidation techniques include the use of mind maps or flash cards.

The key to these techniques is that you will be thinking actively about the information you are revising. This increases the chance of you remembering it and also allows you to see links between different topic areas. Developing this kind of deep, holistic understanding of the core concepts is the key to getting top marks in the exam.

Complete practice exam questions

Completing practice exam questions is a crucial part of your revision. It allows you to practise applying your knowledge to the exam questions and to see if your revision is working. A useful strategy is to complete questions on a topic that you have not yet fully revised. This will show you which areas of the topic you know already and which areas you need to work on. You can then revise the topic and go back and complete the questions again to check that you have successfully plugged the gaps in your knowledge.

Use technology

There are many creative ways to use technology to help you revise. For example, you can make slideshows of key points, shoot short videos or record podcasts. The advantage of doing this is that by creating the resource you are thinking about a particular topic in detail. This will help you to remember it and improve your understanding. You will also have the finished product, which you can revisit closer to the exam. You could even pass on what you have made to your friends to help them.

Content Guidance

■ Chemical elements are joined together to form biological compounds

The study of biochemistry is fundamental to biology. Many students find it a difficult topic but it is important to persevere as it can earn you some fairly straightforward marks in the exam. This section looks at the biological importance of some key inorganic ions, water and monomers and polymers, and then moves on to the three main classes of chemical you need to study: carbohydrates, lipid and proteins.

Key inorganic ions

You need to know some examples of inorganic ions and their function in living organisms:
- magnesium (Mg^{2+}) — used to form the green photosynthetic pigment chlorophyll
- iron (Fe^{2+}) — a component of haemoglobin, which is used to carry oxygen in the blood
- calcium (Ca^{2+}) — used to strengthen bones and teeth and cell walls in plants
- phosphate (PO_4^{3-}) — used to form phospholipids, which make up cell membranes

Water

Water is vital to all life on Earth. Water's properties arise from the chemical structure of the water molecule. A water molecule consists of two hydrogen atoms bonded to an oxygen atom.

Water is known as a **polar molecule** because it has a slightly uneven distribution of charge. The hydrogen atoms of the water molecule are slightly positively charged, while the oxygen atom is slightly negatively charged.

This slight uneven distribution of charge allows **hydrogen bonds** to form between a hydrogen atom of one water molecule and the oxygen atom of another water molecule. These hydrogen bonds create a force known as cohesion, which 'sticks' the water molecules together. Hydrogen bonding between water molecules is shown in Figure 1.

Cohesion forces are responsible for the high **surface tension** of water and the formation of a 'skin' at the point where the water meets the air. This skin allows some organisms such as pond skaters and basilisks to literally walk on water. Cohesion also allows the transport of long columns of water up the stem in the xylem of plants as part of the transpiration stream.

Water is also known as a **universal solvent** as it dissolves a wide variety of different solutes. This is important for two reasons:
- It means chemical reactions can occur in solution.
- It makes transport inside living organisms much easier. Solutes are able to dissolve, for example in the blood, and then be carried around the organism.

Knowledge check 1

When plants do not have enough magnesium, their leaves can become yellow. Explain why this happens.

Exam tip

It is important to answer exam questions as precisely as possible. In one exam question, just writing 'calcium makes up teeth' was not awarded the mark. Students had to say that calcium *strengthened* the teeth.

Knowledge check 2

Why is water described as a polar molecule?

Knowledge check 3

Why are there cohesion forces between water molecules?

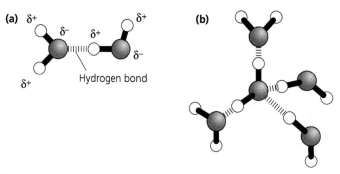

Figure 1 (a) The charges on water molecules and (b) a cluster of water molecules

Water is used in a variety of chemical reactions within living organisms, including photosynthesis and hydrolysis reactions.

Water has a very high **specific heat capacity**. This means that it takes a large amount of energy to raise the temperature of a body of water. This is important in cells because it means that a relatively large amount of heat is required to raise a cell's temperature. This allows the cell to maintain a relatively stable internal temperature, which is important for the actions of enzymes within the cell. The high specific heat capacity of water is also important in bodies of water such as lakes and ponds, where it provides a relatively stable environment for aquatic animals.

Water has a high **latent heat of evaporation**. This means that a relatively large amount of energy is required to turn water from a liquid into a gas. This is important for living organisms as the evaporation of water (e.g. during sweating) takes energy away from the skin and causes a cooling effect.

Solid water has a lower density than liquid water, so solid ice floats on top of liquid water. This is important because when ice forms it provides an insulating layer on the top of a body of water. The liquid water beneath the solid ice has a higher temperature than the air above it, allowing aquatic organisms to survive even if the water at the surface has frozen.

Water's transparency is also important for living organisms. It allows light to travel through it, which means that organisms such as plants and algae are able to photosynthesise.

Water is a metabolite, a reactant in photosynthesis and hydrolysis, and a product of respiration and condensation reactions. Water also provides support and buoyancy for aquatic organisms.

> **Exam tip**
>
> If you are talking about the advantages to living organisms of water being transparent, make sure you are specific. Answers such as 'it lets light get to plants' or 'it allows fish to see' will not earn you any marks.

Monomers and polymers

Carbohydrates and proteins form polymers. A polymer is a large molecule made up of repeating units called **monomers**. Polymers are formed in polymerisation reactions. These are reactions that join monomers together to make a polymer. In the polymers you need to study, condensation reactions join the monomers together. Hydrolysis reactions break the bonds in a polymer, releasing the monomers.

> **Knowledge check 4**
>
> Why is water known as a universal solvent?

> **Knowledge check 5**
>
> What property of water means that cells have a relatively consistent internal temperature?

> **Knowledge check 6**
>
> What is the advantage to organisms of water's high latent heat?

> **Exam tip**
>
> Students often get confused between 'high specific heat' and 'high latent heat'. Make sure you are clear about the difference between these two terms.

Polymers Large molecules made up of repeating units of monomers.

Condensation A chemical reaction involving the joining together of two molecules and the removal of a molecule of water.

Hydrolysis The splitting of a large molecule into smaller molecules by the addition of water.

Carbohydrates

Carbohydrates are important chemicals in biology. They range from simple sugars like glucose to large complex polymers such as chitin. All carbohydrates contain the elements:

- carbon
- hydrogen
- oxygen

It is important to know the number of bonds that each of the atoms above form in a molecule. This information will then allow you to check any structural diagrams you have drawn to make sure they are correct. Carbon atoms form four bonds, hydrogen forms one bond and oxygen atoms form two bonds.

Monosaccharides

The basic unit of a carbohydrate is a **monosaccharide**. All monosaccharides have the general formula $C_nH_{2n}O_n$.

This means that in a monosaccharide there is the same number of carbon atoms as oxygen atoms and twice as many hydrogen atoms as carbon atoms. Monosaccharides can be classified by the number of carbon atoms they contain:

- three carbon atoms — triose sugars
- five carbon atoms — pentose sugars (e.g. deoxyribose found in DNA)
- six carbon atoms — hexose sugars (e.g. glucose)

We will focus on the hexose sugars and in particular on glucose. Other hexose sugars include fructose and galactose.

Glucose

Glucose is fundamentally important in biology. It is used in respiration to produce ATP (chemical energy currency used in cells) and it is the monomer for many different polysaccharides. Glucose has two isomers: alpha (α) glucose and beta (β) glucose (Figure 2). Isomers are molecules that have the same chemical formula but a different structure. The only difference between the structures of α-glucose and β-glucose is the different arrangement of the H and OH (hydroxyl group) on carbon 1.

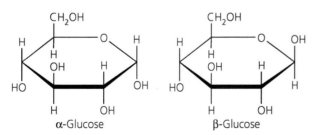

α-Glucose   β-Glucose

Figure 2 The two isomers of glucose

Disaccharides

Two monosaccharides can be joined by a glycosidic bond to form a disaccharide. This reaction is known as a condensation reaction. In a condensation reaction, a molecule of water is produced when the bond is formed. The bond shown in Figure 3 is called

> **Exam tip**
>
> You will not be asked to draw glucose from scratch in the exam, but you may have to annotate a diagram to show the bonds forming or to illustrate the difference between it and another molecule, so it is worth learning its structure.

> **Exam tip**
>
> Students often have trouble explaining the difference between α-glucose and β-glucose. Saying that the H and OH are arranged differently on carbon 1 is better than talking about up, down etc.

a 1,4 glycosidic bond because it forms between carbons 1 and 4. When two glucose molecules are joined by a 1,4 glycosidic bond, the disaccharide **maltose** is formed, as shown in Figure 3.

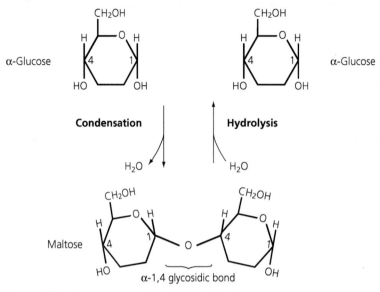

Figure 3 The formation and hydrolysis of maltose

A hydrolysis reaction can be used to break the chemical bond formed in a condensation reaction. In a hydrolysis reaction, the bond is broken by the chemical insertion of water. If the glycosidic bond in maltose is broken by a hydrolysis reaction, two molecules of glucose are formed.

Table 1 shows the disaccharides formed when different monosaccharides are joined by condensation reactions.

Monosaccharides	Disaccharide
Glucose + glucose	Maltose
Glucose + fructose	Sucrose
Glucose + galactose	Lactose

Table 1 Disaccharides formed when different monosaccharides are joined by condensation reactions

Polysaccharides

Three or more monosaccharides can be joined by condensation reactions to form a polysaccharide. The monosaccharides are the monomers and the polysaccharide is a polymer. Most polysaccharides contain thousands of monomers.

Polysaccharides generally either have a structural function or are used to store glucose. The large size of polysaccharides means that they are insoluble, which is important for them to be able to carry out their functions. They are also osmotically inactive. This means that they can be stored in cells without any detrimental osmotic effects. In the case of the storage of polysaccharides, it is important that glucose can be removed easily.

Exam tip

The carbon atoms are not shown in Figure 2, which is a common, simplified way of drawing glucose. However, two carbon atoms are labelled in Figure 3. Here, the numbers are important because they allow you to identify which carbon atoms in a molecule form bonds (in this case, 1 and 4).

Exam tip

When drawing a diagram to show a condensation reaction forming a bond, don't forget to draw in the water molecule that is produced — it is often worth a mark.

Knowledge check 7

What are the products of the hydrolysis of maltose?

Polysaccharides Three or more monosaccharides joined by condensation reactions.

Storage polysaccharides

The two main storage polysaccharides are starch and glycogen.

- **Starch** is a polymer made up of a large number of α-glucose monomers. Starch has two components, **amylose** and **amylopectin**. Amylose is a chain of glucose monomers joined by 1,4 glycosidic bonds and formed into a helix. The structure of amylose is shown in Figure 4.

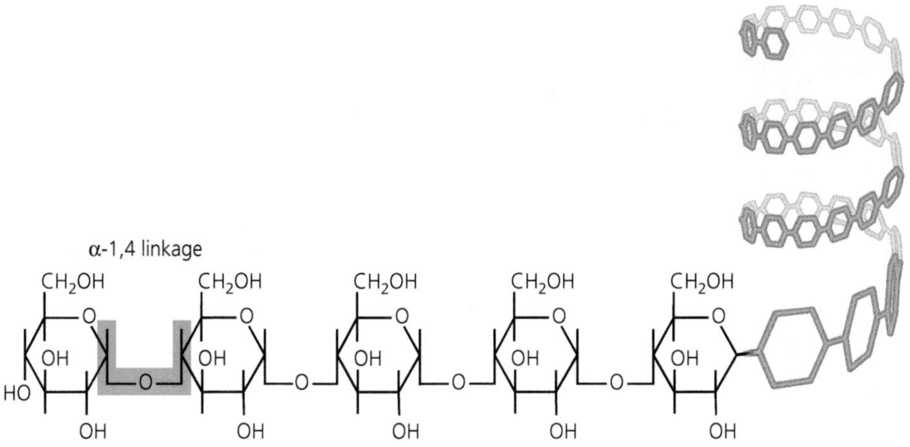

Knowledge check 8

Why is it important that polysaccharides that have a structural function are insoluble?

Figure 4 The structure of amylose

Amylopectin has both 1,4 and 1,6 glycosidic bonds. This gives it a branched structure. The structure of amylopectin is shown in Figure 5. Starch is used to store glucose in plants.

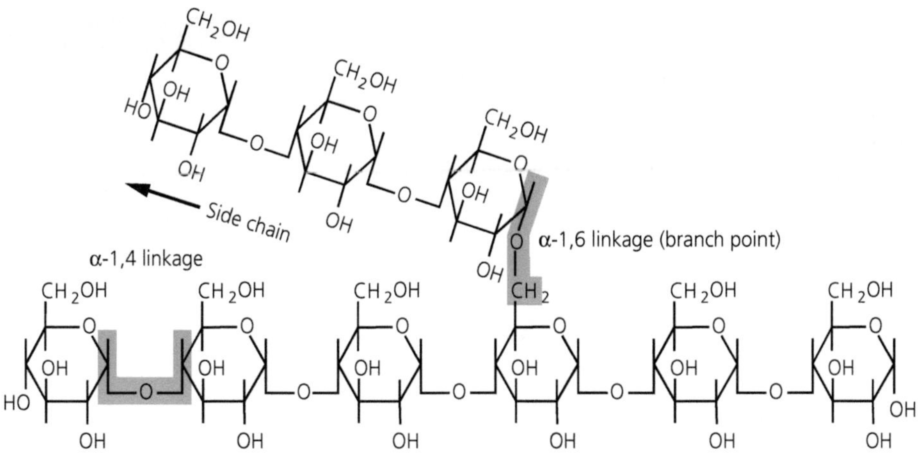

Figure 5 The structure of a branched polysaccharide: amylopectin and glycogen

Knowledge check 9

Which polysaccharide is used for storage in animals?

- **Glycogen** is a polymer made up of a large number of α-glucose monomers. Like amylopectin, it has both 1,4 and 1,6 glycosidic bonds, so it has a branched structure. Glycogen is used to store glucose in animals and is found in muscle cells.

Cellulose

Cellulose is a polymer made up of β-glucose monomers. The β-glucose monomers are joined by 1,4 glycosidic bonds and are arranged into long straight chains. Each β-glucose molecule is rotated 180° from the previous molecule in the chain. This enables hydrogen bonds to form between the OH groups in adjacent chains. The structure of cellulose is shown in Figure 6.

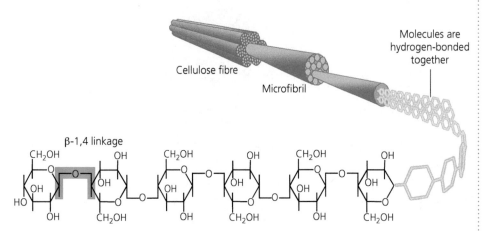

Figure 6 The structure of cellulose

Many cellulose chains form a microfibril and many microfibrils form a cellulose fibre. Cellulose fibres make up the cell walls of plants. The large number of hydrogen bonds in cellulose gives it high tensile strength. This makes the cell wall strong and rigid and prevents the cell from bursting.

Chitin

Chitin is made up of chains of β monomers, rotated 180° from the previous monomer, with hydrogen bonds between chains forming microfibrils. Some OH groups of the β monomers are replaced by nitrogen-containing acetylamine groups. Chitin is strong and lightweight and is used to form the exoskeletons of insects.

Biochemical tests for carbohydrates

Starch test

1 Add several drops of iodine solution (iodine dissolved in potassium iodide) to the sample.
2 If starch is present, the sample turns blue/black.

Benedict's test for reducing sugar

1 Add Benedict's reagent to the sample.
2 Boil the solution.
3 If a reducing sugar is present, a brick-red precipitate forms.

All monosaccharides are reducing sugars and so are some disaccharides such as maltose.

Knowledge check 10

Which monomer makes up cellulose?

Knowledge check 11

Which bonds give cellulose fibres their strength?

Knowledge check 12

How does chitin differ from other polysaccharides?

Exam tip

It is easy to get confused with which monomer makes up which polysaccharide. A simple way to remember it is that the storage polysaccharides have α-glucose monomers, whereas the structural polysaccharides have β-glucose monomers.

Benedict's test for non-reducing sugar

If the reducing sugar test returns a negative result, a further test can be carried out to determine whether a non-reducing sugar (such as sucrose) is present in the sample. A non-reducing sugar can be identified by first hydrolysing the glycosidic bond in the molecule, forming two monosaccharides. The monosaccharides will then produce a positive result when boiled with Benedict's reagent. The glycosidic bond is hydrolysed by heating the non-reducing sugar with acid.

1   Check that there is no reducing sugar present by heating part of the sample with Benedict's reagent (see above).

2   Using a separate sample, heat with dilute hydrochloric acid.

3   Neutralise by adding sodium hydrogen carbonate.

4   Add Benedict's reagent to the sample.

5   Boil the solution.

6   If a non-reducing sugar was present in the original sample, a brick-red precipitate forms.

Lipids

Lipids are made up of the same elements as carbohydrates — carbon, hydrogen and oxygen. However, unlike carbohydrates, lipids are not made up of monomers that link together to form polymers. Instead, they consist of two molecules: glycerol and fatty acids. Glycerol is found in all lipids (Figure 7).

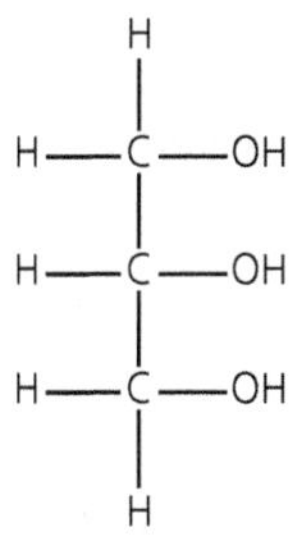

Fatty acids consist of a methyl group, a variable length hydrocarbon chain and a carboxyl group. The hydrocarbon chain contains an even number of carbon atoms — between 14 and 22. Fatty acids are either **saturated** or **unsaturated**. Saturated fatty acids have no carbon–carbon double bonds in the hydrocarbon chain. Unsaturated fatty acids do have carbon–carbon double bonds within the hydrocarbon chain (Figure 8). Monounsaturated fatty acids have one carbon–carbon double bond and polyunsaturated fatty acids contain two or more carbon–carbon double bonds. Saturated fatty acids are found in animal fats and unsaturated fatty acids are found in plant oils.

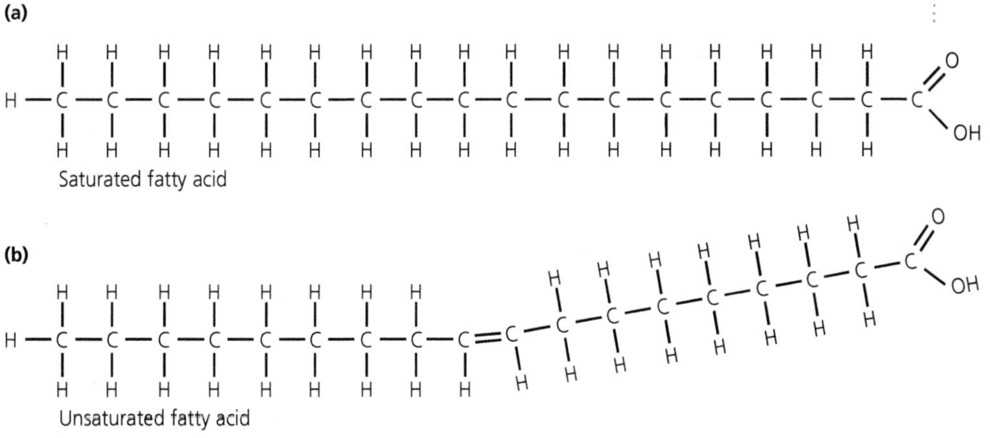

> **Exam tip**
>
> Biochemical tests do come up in exams. For each test, make sure you know:
> ■ the name of the test
> ■ how to carry out the test
> ■ the positive result

Figure 7 Glycerol

(a)

Saturated fatty acid

(b)

Unsaturated fatty acid

Figure 8 (a) A saturated fatty acid and (b) an unsaturated fatty acid with one double bond

Three fatty acids combine chemically with one glycerol molecule to form a **triglyceride**. There are three condensation reactions (one for each fatty acid) which form three **ester bonds**. In Figure 9, the fatty acid's hydrocarbon chain is drawn in a simplified form as a zigzag line. In this reaction, each OH group on the glycerol molecule loses a hydrogen atom while the carboxyl group of the fatty acid loses an OH to form three molecules of water.

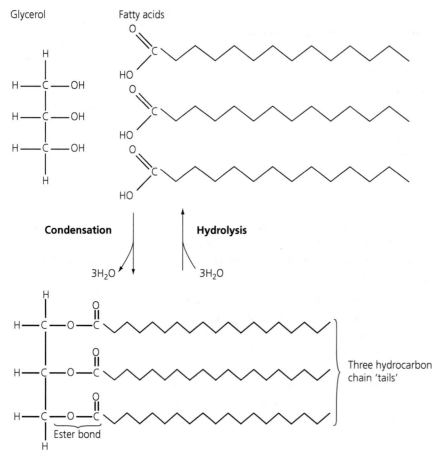

Figure 9 Formation and hydrolysis of a triglyceride

Phospholipids

Phospholipids are a special type of lipid. Two fatty acids combine with a glycerol molecule. The other OH group on the glycerol forms a bond with a phosphate group. This makes the 'head' (glycerol and phosphate) of the molecule hydrophilic and the 'tail' (the two fatty acids) hydrophobic. This property is important in the formation of cell membranes. Figure 10 shows the structure of a phospholipid.

Exam tip

When answering exam questions, try to give the best possible answer, rather than just saying that lipids are used for energy storage. Talk also about *why* they are a more efficient energy store than carbohydrates.

Knowledge check 13

How does a saturated fatty acid differ from an unsaturated fatty acid?

Triglyceride Three fatty acids molecules that are linked by condensation to a molecule of glycerol.

Ester bond A chemical bond formed as a result of condensation between glycerol and a fatty acid. There are three of these bonds in a triglyceride molecule.

Exam tip

You will not be asked to draw the whole triglyceride structure, but you could be asked to show how the fatty acids bond with the glycerol, so make sure you learn this structure. It is important also to remember that the water molecules formed are made from the OH group of the fatty acid and the H from the glycerol.

Knowledge check 14

What is the bond in a triglyceride called?

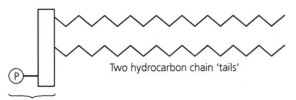

Glycerol–phosphate 'head'

Figure 10 A phospholipid

Lipids have a variety of functions in living organisms:

■ energy storage — a lipid stores twice as much energy as the same mass of carbohydrates, making it an efficient store of energy; lipids are used in seeds to store energy
■ protection of delicate organs
■ thermal insulation
■ buoyancy in aquatic organisms
■ a source of metabolic water for organisms such as camels that live in low water environments

Lipids are insoluble in water but soluble in organic solvents such as acetone and ethanol. Saturated fats are solid at room temperature. Unsaturated oils are liquid at room temperature and are found in plants.

A high intake of fat by humans, particularly saturated fat, is a contributory factor in heart disease. It raises the low density lipoprotein (LDL) cholesterol level, increasing the risk of atheroma in coronary and other arteries.

Biochemical test for lipids

Lipids can be identified using the emulsion test. Ethanol is added to the sample and shaken thoroughly. Distilled water is then added. If a layer of cloudy white suspension forms, the test is positive and lipids are present in the sample.

Proteins

Proteins are an incredibly varied class of biological molecules. They are made up of the elements carbon, hydrogen, oxygen and nitrogen. They sometimes also contain **sulphur**.

Proteins are polypeptides. A polypeptide is a polymer of **amino acids**. Figure 11 shows an amino acid.

Polypeptide A polymer consisting of a chain of amino acid molecules. They are joined by peptide bonds formed by condensation. One or more polypeptides form a protein.

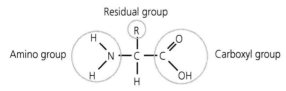

Figure 11 The general structure of an amino acid

Amino acids are made up of an amino group (NH_2), a carboxyl group (COOH) and a variable residual or R group. There are 20 different R groups, giving 20 different amino acids. Two amino acids with different R groups are shown in Figure 12.

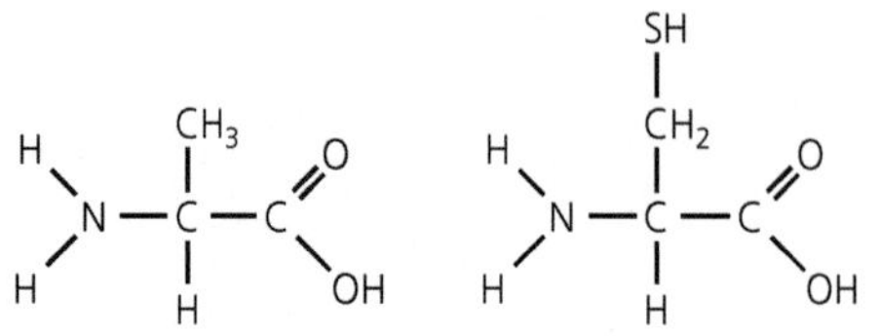

Figure 12 Alanine and cysteine

Knowledge check 15

How many different R groups are there?

Two amino acids combine in a condensation reaction to form a **dipeptide**. A **peptide bond** forms between the carboxyl group of one amino acid and the amino group of the other amino acid. As this is a condensation reaction, a molecule of water is formed. The formation of a dipeptide is shown in Figure 13.

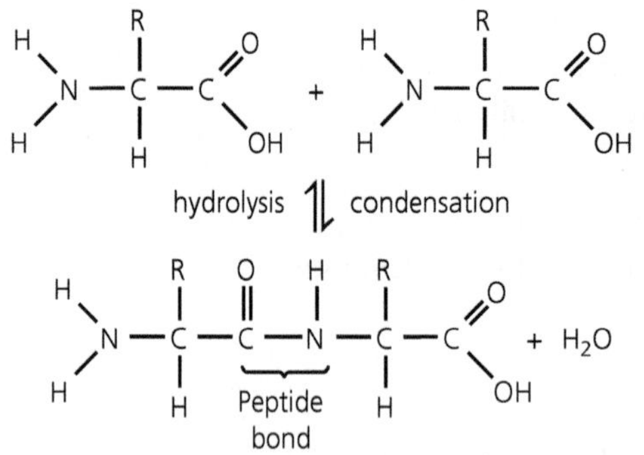

Figure 13 A condensation reaction forms a dipeptide from two amino acids

Protein structure

Three or more amino acids joined by peptide bonds form a polypeptide. The amino acids are the monomers and the polypeptide is the polymer. The type, number and sequence of amino acids in a protein is its **primary structure**. There is a near infinite number of different primary structures.

The polypeptide can twist to form either an α-helix or a β-pleated sheet. This is the **secondary structure** of the protein. The secondary structure's shape is held in place by hydrogen bonds between the peptide bonds.

The polypeptide can fold into specific complex three-dimensional shapes. This is the **tertiary structure** of the protein. This specific structure is maintained by hydrogen bonds, ionic bonds and disulphide bonds between the R groups of the amino acids. These bonds, together with a summary of primary and secondary structures, are shown in Figure 14.

Knowledge check 16

What is the primary structure of a protein?

Knowledge check 17

What are the two types of secondary structure?

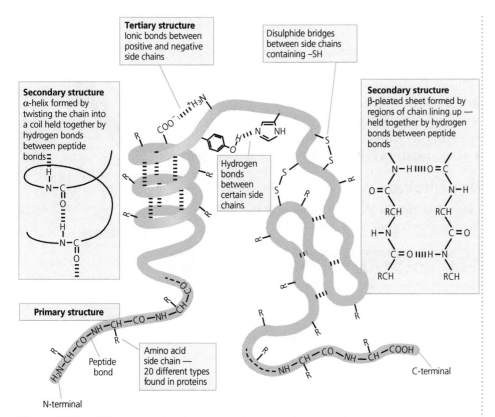

Figure 14 The different levels of structure in a protein molecule

Two or more polypeptides with a tertiary structure can combine to form a **quaternary structure**. An example of a protein with a quaternary structure is haemoglobin. Haemoglobin is made up of four polypeptides (two α-chains and two β-chains) and prosthetic (non-protein) iron-containing haem groups. Haemoglobin is used to transport oxygen in red blood cells. A molecule of haemoglobin is shown in Figure 15.

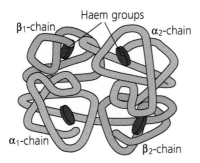

Figure 15 A haemoglobin molecule

Exam tip

Make sure that you can recognise all three types of bond found in the tertiary structure of a protein in a diagram. Don't forget that all polypeptides have peptide bonds between their amino acids.

Knowledge check 18

Give an example of a protein that has a quaternary structure.

Fibrous and globular proteins

Generally, proteins can be divided into two types: fibrous or globular.

- **Fibrous proteins** are structural proteins that have a secondary structure. They are insoluble. Examples of fibrous proteins include keratin and collagen. Keratin is used to form hair and nails and collagen is used to form tendons. Collagen consists of three α-helix chains formed into long strands (Figure 16).

- **Globular proteins** have a tertiary or quaternary structure and a metabolic function. They are soluble in water and examples include enzymes and hormones.

Biochemical test for proteins

Proteins can be identified using the biuret test. A small volume of biuret reagent is added to the sample. If the sample contains protein, it turns violet.

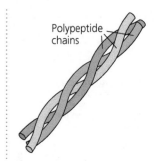

Figure 16 A collagen molecule

Exam tip

Make sure you learn the features of fibrous and globular proteins.

Practical work

- *Food tests to include: iodine–potassium iodide test for starch; Benedict's test for reducing and non-reducing sugars; biuret test for protein; emulsion test for fats and oils.*

For each test, make sure you know the method and the positive results.

Summary

After studying this topic, you should be able to:
- give examples of the key inorganic ions and their importance to living organisms
- explain the biological importance of water and relate some of its properties to the fact that it is a polar molecule that forms hydrogen bonds
- explain bond formation and breaking by condensation and hydrolysis reactions
- describe carbohydrates in terms of monosaccharides, disaccharides and polysaccharides and explain the structure of examples of each
- explain how triglycerides form from fatty acids and glycerol and describe the differences between a saturated and an unsaturated fatty acid

- give examples of the functions of lipids in living organisms
- explain how a phospholipid differs from a triglyceride
- describe the structure of amino acids, dipeptides and polypeptides
- explain the four levels of protein structure and give the bonds found in each level
- distinguish between fibrous and globular proteins
- describe the biochemical tests for carbohydrates, lipids and proteins, and be able to identify the positive results

Cell structure and organisation

Cells are the basic units of living organisms. The cells you need to study can be divided into two types: **eukaryotes** (animal and plant cells) and **prokaryotes** (bacteria).

Eukaryotes

Eukaryotes are internally divided by membranes. These membranes are important because they:

- provide a surface to which enzymes can attach and on which chemical reactions can occur
- keep potentially harmful chemicals or enzymes contained, stopping them from damaging or breaking down structures in the cell
- act as a transport system

There are many different types of eukaryote cell. For the exam, you need to study animal and plant cells in detail. Figure 17 shows the structure of an animal cell.

Eukaryote An organism or cell that contains a nucleus and other organelles enclosed by membranes.

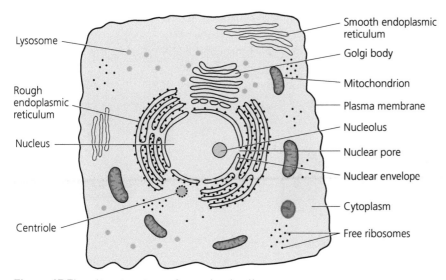

Figure 17 The ultrastructure of an animal cell

Eukaryotes have an exterior plasma (cell-surface) membrane that encloses the cytoplasm of the cell. The cytoplasm is a gel-like substance that contains the cell's **organelles**. These are the internal structures within the cell.

Organelles in animal and plant cells

Animal and plant cells contain the following organelles.

Nucleus

The **nucleus** contains the cell's **DNA**. This is the genetic material that is passed on from one generation of an organism to the next and provides the code for the synthesis of proteins. For most of a eukaryote's life, the DNA remains inside the nucleus. To allow protein synthesis to occur, a strand of messenger RNA (mRNA) is made using DNA as a template (transcription, see p. 47). This mRNA strand then leaves the nucleus to carry the code for protein synthesis to the cytoplasm.

The **nuclear membrane** (also called the **nuclear envelope**) encloses the nucleus. This double membrane contains small 'gaps' known as nuclear pores. These allow the mRNA to exit the nucleus and travel to the cytoplasm. The interior of the nucleus contains a cytoplasm-like material known as the nucleoplasm. Within the nucleoplasm is the cell's DNA in the form of **chromatin**.

The nucleus also contains the **nucleolus**, which produces ribosomal RNA (rRNA).

Mitochondria

Mitochondria (singular: **mitochondrion**) release chemical energy in the form of ATP during aerobic (requiring oxygen) respiration. Like the nucleus, mitochondria have a double membrane. This consists of an outer membrane, an intermembrane space and an inner membrane. The inner membrane is folded to form the cristae. These folds increase the surface area on which ATP synthesis can occur.

Knowledge check 19

What is the function of the mitochondria?

Inside the mitochondria is a cytoplasm-like **matrix**. This contains ribosomes and the mitochondrial DNA. This DNA allows the mitochondria to divide to meet the needs of the cell, separate from the normal replication cycle of the cell. Mitochondrial DNA is evidence that the mitochondria may have once been free-living organisms that were ingested by the ancestors of eukaryote cells and have lived inside eukaryotes ever since. Figure 18 shows the structure of a mitochondrion.

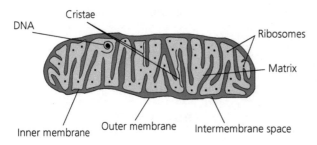

Figure 18 The structure of a mitochondrion

Knowledge check 20

Why is it important that the cristae give the mitochondria a large internal surface area?

Endoplasmic reticulum

Rough endoplasmic reticulum (RER) consists of a series of membranes that are linked to the nuclear membrane. The rough endoplasmic reticulum is used as a transport system for proteins and has ribosomes along its length (which is why it is known as 'rough' endoplasmic reticulum). The ribosomes carry out protein synthesis (translation, see pp. 48–49). Ribosomes are also found free in the cytoplasm.

Smooth endoplasmic reticulum (SER) is a series of membranes that do not have ribosomes on their surface (hence, 'smooth'). The smooth endoplasmic reticulum is involved in the synthesis of lipids.

Knowledge check 21

Why is rough endoplasmic reticulum described as 'rough'?

Ribosomes

Ribosomes have two subunits, large and small. The subunits come together around a strand of mRNA, which fits into the mRNA groove. Ribosomes are made up of protein and rRNA.

Golgi body

The **Golgi body** (also known as the **Golgi apparatus**) is a stack of flattened membranous sacs. The Golgi body has a variety of functions, including the formation of glycoproteins and lysosomes, but its main role is modifying and packaging proteins to be exported from the cell. This process is described below and shown in Figure 19.

1 Vesicles (small, membrane-bound sacs) containing proteins formed by the rough endoplasmic reticulum fuse at one end of the Golgi sacs.

2 The protein is modified inside the Golgi sacs.

3 The modified protein is budded off in a vesicle at the other end of the Golgi sacs.

4 The vesicle containing the modified protein travels to the cell's outer plasma membrane where the protein is released by exocytosis. The process of exocytosis is discussed in more detail on page 29.

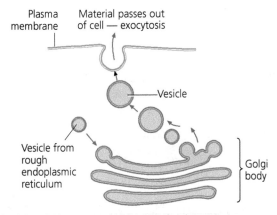

Figure 19 The Golgi body's role in processing and packaging substances produced by a cell

Organelles in animal cells

Animal cells also contain the following organelles.

Lysosomes

Lysosomes are vesicles containing digestive enzymes. They can be used to break down worn-out organelles and to digest material taken in by phagocytosis. The action of a lysosome is as follows:

1 The material is taken into the cell and trapped in a vacuole.

2 The lysosomes fuse with the membrane of the vacuole and release their digestive enzymes into the vacuole.

3 The digestive enzymes break down the material.

Centrioles

Centrioles are small cylinders that separate from each other during the early stages of mitosis to form the spindle fibres. This is discussed in more detail on page 52.

Organelles in plant cells

Plant cells also contain the following organelles. The structure of a plant cell is shown in Figure 20.

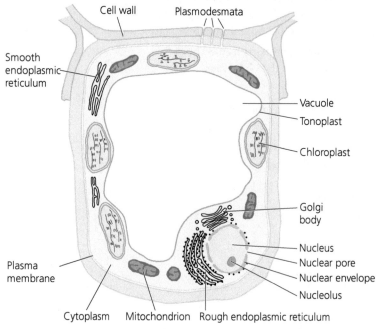

Figure 20 A generalised plant cell viewed with an electron microscope

Chloroplasts

Chloroplasts are large organelles that have a double membrane (like the nucleus and mitochondria) and are the site of **photosynthesis**. This is the process by which sugars and other organic molecules are formed from carbon dioxide and water using energy from sunlight.

Within the chloroplasts is a cytoplasm-like material called the **stroma**. Within the stroma are many membrane-bound compartments called **thylakoids**. The membrane of the thylakoids contains the pigment **chlorophyll**, which absorbs the light energy used in photosynthesis. Thylakoids form stacks called grana (singular: granum), which are linked by lamellae (singular: lamella). The stroma also contains starch grains and ribosomes.

Like mitochondria, chloroplasts also contain ribosomes and chloroplast DNA. As with mitochondrial DNA, this chloroplast DNA is evidence that chloroplasts were once free-living organisms ingested by the ancestors of plant cells. Figure 21 shows the structure of a chloroplast.

Exam tip

Note that the three organelles that have a double membrane are the nucleus, mitochondrion and chloroplast.

Knowledge check 22

What is the photosynthetic pigment in the thylakoid called?

Exam tip

Chloroplasts and mitochondria have similar structures but do not confuse the two. For example, the chloroplast does not have a matrix.

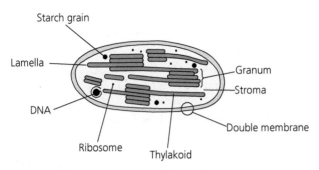

Figure 21 The structure of a chloroplast

Other features of plant cells

Plant cells also have a **cellulose cell wall**. This keeps the plant cell rigid and prevents it from bursting. The plant cell wall has many pores called **plasmodesmata**. These allow the cytoplasm of neighbouring cells to connect, enabling substances to pass between plant cells.

Plants cells also have a large permanent vacuole, which contains cell sap. It is surrounded by a membrane called the **tonoplast**. The vacuole is used for storage and helps to support the plant cell. Animal cells may also contain vacuoles, but they are much smaller and do not have a tonoplast.

Prokaryotes

Prokaryotes are cells that contain no membrane-bound organelles. Their DNA is not enclosed in the nucleus, but is free in the cytoplasm. Most prokaryotes are significantly smaller than eukaryotes (1–10 μm in length as opposed to 10–100 μm in length for eukaryotes). Bacteria are examples of prokaryotes. Figure 22 shows the features of a prokaryote.

Prokaryote A single-celled organism that has no nuclear membrane or any other membrane-bound organelles.

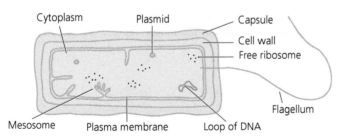

Figure 22 The features of a prokaryote

Prokaryotes have the following features:
- capsule — the outer layer
- murein cell wall — the cell wall of a prokaryote is made from murein (peptidoglycan) not cellulose. This prevents the cell from bursting
- mesosome — an infolding of the prokaryote's plasma membrane. The infolding increases the surface area for respiration and other chemical reactions to occur

- DNA — the DNA is free in the cytoplasm in an area known as the nucleoid. Prokaryote DNA is usually found in a single circular chromosome. Prokaryotes may also have small circular pieces of DNA called plasmids
- ribosomes — like eukaryotes, prokaryotes contain ribosomes. However, the ribosomes of prokaryotes are significantly smaller than the ribosomes found in eukaryotes
- flagellum — prokaryotes sometimes have a flagellum, which allows them to move

Viruses

Viruses contain no cytoplasm and so they are not considered to be cells. They are generally thought not even to be alive. Viruses infect both prokaryotes and eukaryotes. They consist of nucleic acid and a protein coat. In most viruses that infect eukaryotes, the nucleic acid is RNA, whereas in most viruses that infect bacteria (bacteriophages), the nucleic acid is DNA.

Tissues, organs and organ systems

A **tissue** is a group of cells that have a similar structure and they work together to perform a particular function. Examples of animal tissues include:

- **epithelial tissue**, e.g. ciliated, columnar and squamous epithelia — epithelial tissue lines the spaces in animals such as the digestive and respiratory system
- **muscle**, e.g. smooth, striated and cardiac muscle — muscle tissue contracts and relaxes to move parts of animals
- **connective tissue**, e.g. collagen — structural tissue in animals

Xylem and phloem are examples of plant tissues.

Different tissues can combine to form **organs**, which carry out a common function. Examples of organs in animals include the brain and the heart. Roots and leaves are examples of plant organs.

An **organ system** is made up of two or more organs working together to perform a life function, such as the respiratory system or digestive system in mammals.

Electron micrographs

The diagrams we draw of cells are simplified to aid understanding. When observing cells under a light microscope, the organelles (with the exception of the nucleus) are not visible. However, using an electron microscope it is possible to produce images showing the organelles. You could be asked to identify the structures shown on an electron micrograph, so make sure you are familiar with this type of image.

> **Exam tip**
>
> A common exam question is to compare the structures of eukaryotes and prokaryotes. Make sure you learn the structures of both types of cell thoroughly and don't make any obvious mistakes, such as stating that they both have cell walls made of cellulose.

> **Exam tip**
>
> You must be able to use and manipulate the magnification formula:
>
> $$\text{magnification} = \frac{\text{image size}}{\text{actual size}}$$
>
> This could be tested in a question looking at electron micrographs.

Practical work

■ *Calibration of the light microscope at low and high power, including calculation of actual size of a structure and the magnification of a structure in a drawing.*

This is an important skill to accurately measure samples on microscope slides. Make sure you are comfortable using the eye-piece graticule and the stage micrometer as you could be asked to do a calibration in an exam paper question.

■ *Preparation and scientific drawing of a slide of living cells, including calculation of actual size and magnification of drawing.*

This is a common subject for exam questions, so ensure you are comfortable applying and rearranging the magnification formula.

Summary

After studying this topic, you should be able to:

■ explain the importance of the internal membranes to eukaryote cells

■ label all the organelles found in animal, plant and prokaryote cells

■ explain the functions of the different parts of the nucleus, mitochondria and chloroplast and label these parts on a diagram

■ explain the functions of the rough endoplasmic reticulum, smooth endoplasmic reticulum, ribosomes, Golgi body, lysosomes, centrioles, vacuole, cell wall and plasmodesmata

■ explain the differences in structure between eukaryotes and prokaryotes, with particular emphasis on the lack of membrane-bound organelles in prokaryotes and the fact that the DNA is free in the cytoplasm

■ describe the basic structure of a virus

■ describe tissues, organs and organ systems and give specific examples of tissues found in animals and plants

Cell membranes and transport

The plasma membrane

The plasma (cell-surface) membrane is the barrier through which all matter entering cells must pass. It has the following functions:

- to give the cell structure
- to allow substances to exit and enter the cell
- cell-to-cell recognition and cell-to-cell signalling

The plasma membrane is selectively permeable, which means it is able to control what enters and exits the cell. It mainly consists of phospholipid molecules arranged into a **bilayer** (a double layer). Under the electron microscope and when stained with a water-soluble dye, the plasma membrane appears as a double line. This is because the hydrophilic 'heads' of the phospholipid molecules take up the dye. The distance across the membrane is 7–8 nm.

The hydrophilic heads of the phospholipid molecules face outwards and the hydrophobic tails face inwards. This forms a hydrophobic, non-polar region in the middle of the bilayer. This prevents polar molecules such as glucose from passing through. The structure of the plasma membrane is shown in Figure 23.

Phospholipid A molecule made up of a hydrophilic glycerol–phosphate 'head' and two fatty acid 'tails' forming a hydrophobic tail.

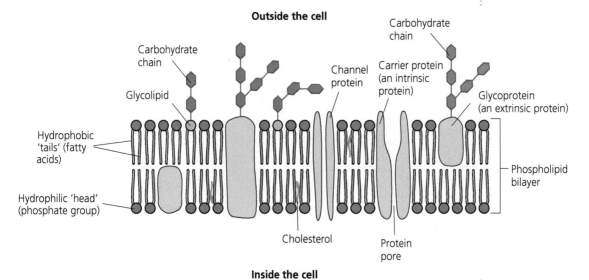

Figure 23 The structure of the plasma membrane

The plasma membrane also contains proteins. They are divided into two types:

- **intrinsic proteins** lie across both the layers of the membrane (e.g. a carrier protein)
- **extrinsic proteins** are either in one layer of the membrane or on the surface of the membrane (e.g. a glycoprotein or glycocalyx)

Knowledge check 23

How does an intrinsic protein differ from an extrinsic protein?

Glycoproteins are proteins with a carbohydrate chain attached. Glycolipids are lipids with a carbohydrate chain attached. Both glycoproteins and glycolipids are involved in cell-to-cell recognition. The plasma membrane of animal cells also contains cholesterol, which helps to increase its rigidity.

When temperature increases, the molecules that make up the membrane gain kinetic energy and move at a faster rate. This causes the membrane to become more fluid (the components are more free to move) and therefore more permeable. In an experimental setting, organic solvents (such as ethanol) can be used to dissolve the phospholipids and so increase the permeability of the membrane.

The plasma membrane is best described by the **fluid mosaic model** proposed by Singer and Nicholson:
- fluid — all parts of the membrane can move relative to each other
- mosaic — the proteins are dotted throughout the membrane like mosaic tiles

Transport across the membrane

There are several ways in which substances can move across the plasma membrane.

Diffusion

Diffusion is the movement of molecules or ions from an area of higher concentration to an area of lower concentration (down a concentration gradient).

Diffusion occurs through the phospholipid bilayer. Due to the hydrophobic tails of the phospholipids, only lipid-soluble molecules, which are non-polar and uncharged, can pass through the phospholipid bilayer. Proteins are not involved. As the movement is down the concentration gradient, chemical energy in the form of ATP is not needed. Examples of molecules that diffuse through the phospholipid bilayer include oxygen and carbon dioxide.

Facilitated diffusion

Large, water-soluble, polar and charged molecules or ions cannot pass through the hydrophobic tails of the phospholipid bilayer, so they must move through the plasma membrane by **facilitated diffusion**. This involves the molecule or ion moving through a carrier protein or a hydrophilic pore within a channel protein. As this is a type of diffusion, movement of the molecules is again from a high concentration to a low concentration and it does not require chemical energy in the form of ATP. An example of a molecule that moves across the membrane by facilitated diffusion is glucose. Diffusion and facilitated diffusion are shown in Figure 24.

The graphs in Figure 25 show the effect of difference in concentration across a membrane on the rates of diffusion and facilitated diffusion. As can be seen from the graph showing rate of diffusion, as the concentration difference between the inside and the outside of the cell increases, the rate of diffusion increases. Increasing temperature, decreasing size and increasing solubility in lipids would also increase the rate of diffusion.

Exam tip

Co-transport is a type of facilitated diffusion by which two substances are simultaneously transported across a membrane by a carrier protein.

Knowledge check 24

How does diffusion differ from facilitated diffusion?

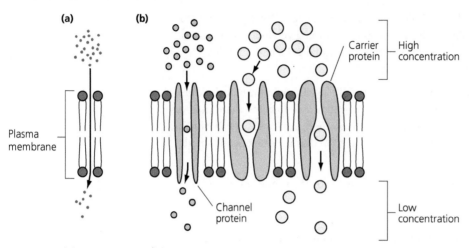

Figure 24 (a) Diffusion and (b) facilitated diffusion

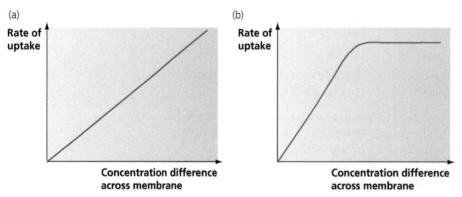

Figure 25 The effect of difference in concentration across a membrane on the rate of (a) diffusion and (b) facilitated diffusion

In facilitated diffusion, as in diffusion, as the concentration difference between the inside and the outside of the cell increases, so does the rate of facilitated diffusion. However, at very high concentration differences the rate of facilitated diffusion reaches a maximum and levels off. This is due to saturation of the carrier proteins or channel proteins in the plasma membrane that are being used for facilitated diffusion, i.e. they are full all the time. Therefore, further increases in the concentration difference between the inside and the outside of the cell do not increase the rate of facilitated diffusion further.

Active transport

Active transport is the movement of molecules or ions from a low concentration to a high concentration (Figure 26). This movement is against the concentration gradient and so chemical energy in the form of ATP is required. A carrier protein in the plasma membrane is used as a pump. An example of active transport is the transport of mineral ions such as nitrates into the root hair cells of plants.

Exam tip

These graphs are similar in shape to some enzyme graphs we will look at later. Don't get the two confused because they represent completely different things.

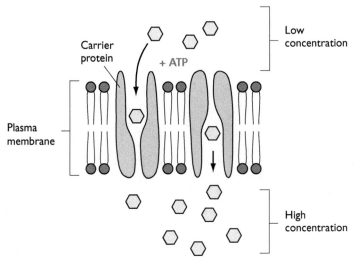

Figure 26 Active transport

In experimental conditions, active transport can be stopped by the addition of a metabolic poison such as cyanide, which stops ATP being produced. As active transport requires ATP, no active transport occurs.

Exocytosis

Large molecules can be released from cells by **exocytosis**. A vesicle fuses with the plasma membrane and the molecule in the vesicle is released to the outside of the cell. An example of this is a modified protein (such as a hormone) being formed in the Golgi body and released by exocytosis. As the vesicle fuses with the plasma membrane, the surface area of the plasma membrane is increased. Exocytosis is important in secretory cells.

Endocytosis

Large substances can be taken into the cell by **endocytosis**. In endocytosis, the plasma membrane folds around the molecule and engulfs it. The substance is then trapped in a vesicle within the cell. Endocytosis can be divided into two categories:
- **phagocytosis** — endocytosis of large solid substance, e.g. a white blood cell ingesting bacteria
- **pinocytosis** — endocytosis of smaller substances, e.g. fluids

As a vesicle is formed from the plasma membrane in endocytosis, it decreases the surface area of the plasma membrane. Figure 27 illustrates the processes of exocytosis and endocytosis.

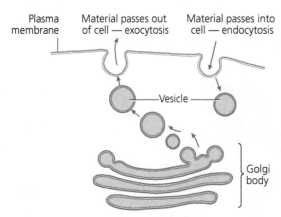

Figure 27 Exocytosis and endocytosis

Osmosis

Water moves across the plasma membrane by osmosis. This is the movement of water molecules from a high water potential to a lower water potential across a partially permeable membrane. Water potential is the potential energy of water relative to pure water. The partially permeable membrane is important in osmosis as it ensures that the solute does not also diffuse and counteract the effect of osmosis.

$$\text{water potential of a cell } (\Psi_{cell}) = \text{solute potential } (\Psi_s) + \text{pressure potential } (\Psi_p)$$

The solute potential (Ψ_s) is generated by the solutes dissolved in the water. The pressure potential (Ψ_p) is the pressure generated by the cytoplasm pushing on the cell wall. As the cell wall is rigid and inelastic, it resists this pressure.

Pure water has a water potential of 0 kPa. This is the highest possible water potential, so all solutions have a negative water potential. Osmosis can be described as movement of water molecules from a solution of less negative water potential to a solution of more negative water potential. During osmosis, the solution with the highest water potential is known as the **hypotonic** solution, whereas the solution with the lower potential is **hypertonic**. Osmosis continues until both solutions have the same water potential. The two solutions will then be **isotonic**. At this point, water still moves but there is no net movement of water (so, overall, the water potentials remain the same).

Plant cells placed in a hypertonic solution will lose water and become flaccid and plasmolysed. **Plasmolysis** is where the cytoplasm shrinks and comes away from the cell wall, causing the plant to wilt. If plants cells are placed in a hypotonic solution, they will gain water, swell and become turgid. This is important as it ensures that plants remain upright. Animal cells placed in a hypertonic solution will lose water and become shrivelled. If animal cells are placed in a hypotonic solution, they will gain water, swell and then burst. Figure 28 summarises the behaviour of plant and animal cells in hypotonic, isotonic and hypertonic solutions.

Incipient plasmolysis is the point at which the cytoplasm begins to come away from the cell wall. It can be found experimentally by observing the solute potential at which half of the plant cells in a sample are plasmolysed. At this point the solute potential is equal to the water potential. This is due to the pressure potential being zero as the cytoplasm is no longer pushing against the cell wall.

Osmosis The movement of water molecules from a high water potential to a lower water potential across a partially permeable membrane.

Exam tip

You must be able to rearrange this equation to work out pressure potential or solute potential. As pressure potentials are always zero or positive and solute and water potentials are always zero or negative, it is easy to spot if you have made a mistake.

Exam tip

It is easy to get confused when working out directions of osmosis. Remember that water always travels from a higher water potential (closer to zero) to a lower water potential (further from zero).

Knowledge check 25

What happens to a plant cell when it is placed in a hypertonic solution?

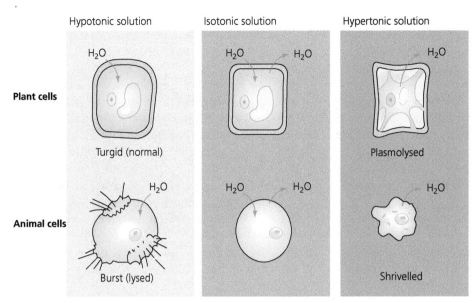

Figure 28 The behaviour of plant and animal cells in hypotonic, isotonic and hypertonic solutions

Practical work

■ *Determination of water potential by measuring changes in mass or length.*

This is a relatively simple practical to carry out, but you should ensure that you can apply the key water potential terms such as plasmolysed, turgid, hypertonic, hypotonic and isotonic to the changes in mass or length.

■ *Determination of solute potential by measuring the degree of incipient plasmolysis.*

The key to this practical is appreciating that at incipient plasmolysis the plasma potential is zero as the cytoplasm is no longer pushing against the cell wall. Therefore, the solute potential is equal to the water potential.

■ *Investigation into the permeability of cell membranes using beetroot.*

This practical relies on the presence of the pigment betalain in beetroot cells. Betalain is unable to pass through the cell membrane. By increasing the membrane's permeability, for example through increasing temperature or the use of organic solvents, the betalain passes out of the beetroot cells and turns the solution they are in red. This change in colour can be measured quantitatively using a colorimeter.

Summary

After studying this topic, you should be able to:

- explain the general functions of a cell's plasma membrane
- describe the structure of the plasma membrane in terms of the fluid mosaic model, to include the phospholipid bilayer, intrinsic and extrinsic proteins, the function of carbohydrate chains and cholesterol
- explain the effect of organic solvents and temperature on the permeability of the plasma membrane
- describe the processes of diffusion, facilitated diffusion and active transport to include examples, direction of movement relative to concentration gradient, ATP requirement and route through the plasma membrane
- explain the processes of exocytosis and endocytosis
- describe osmosis as the movement of water from a high water potential to a lower water potential through a partially permeable membrane
- understand the water potential formula and be able to rearrange it to calculate the pressure and solute potentials
- use the terms hypotonic, hypertonic and isotonic to describe different solutions and be able to state the direction of water movement when given these solutions
- describe and explain the effect of placing plant cells and animal cells in hypotonic and hypertonic solutions

Biological reactions are regulated by enzymes

Enzymes are biological catalysts. They speed up chemical reactions in living organisms and are unchanged at the end of the reactions, which is important because it means that they can be reused. Enzymes are specific — each enzyme catalyses only one reaction.

In order for a reaction to occur, a certain level of **activation energy** is required (Figure 29). Enzymes enable the reaction to occur with a lower activation energy. This means that chemical reactions can occur at high rates even at relatively low temperatures, such as those found in the cells of living organisms. Enzymes can either function **intracellularly** (within cells) or **extracellularly** (outside cells). An example of extracellular enzymes is human digestive enzymes.

Enzymes Proteins that catalyse biological reactions.

Activation energy The amount of energy necessary to bring molecules together so that they will react with each other.

Knowledge check 26

How do enzymes speed up chemical reactions?

Exam tip

Metabolism is a combination of anabolic and metabolic reactions that are catalyzed by enzymes.

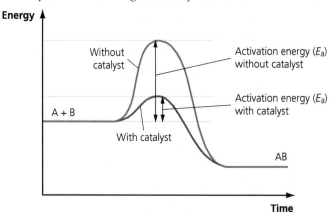

Figure 29 The effect of a catalyst on the activation energy of a reaction

Enzymes are **globular proteins**. They have a specific tertiary structure maintained by hydrogen, disulphide and ionic bonds. They have a region known as an active site. The substrate (the molecule or molecules that are being reacted) enters the active site and an **enzyme–substrate complex** forms. Products form and are then released from the active site. The enzyme is unchanged and is available to catalyse another reaction, as shown in Figure 30. In order for a product to be formed, a successful collision (one with enough activation energy) has to occur between a substrate molecule and the active site of an enzyme.

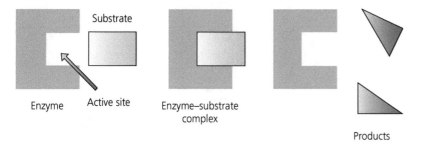

Figure 30 Enzyme action

There are two theories of how enzymes act:

- **The lock and key theory** — the enzyme's active site is a complementary shape to the substrate. The substrate enters the active site and an enzyme–substrate complex is formed. The products then form and leave the active site.
- **The induced-fit theory** — a more recent theory of enzyme action is the induced-fit hypothesis. In this theory, the active site alters its shape slightly to fit the substrate. Again, an enzyme–substrate complex forms and products are released. The enzyme's active site then returns to its original shape. An example of an enzyme that is thought to work using the induced-fit theory is lysozyme. Lysozyme damages bacterial cell walls and can be found in tears and saliva.

Enzyme reaction graphs

Enzyme reactions are often studied by measuring either the concentration of the substrate over time or the concentration of product over time. This allows the rate of the reaction to be calculated. Exam questions on enzymes are often based around graphs that show the results of these investigations. On these graphs the rate of reaction is shown by the gradient of the line. A steeper gradient indicates a faster rate of reaction. Any factor that increases the number of successful collisions between active sites and substrates per unit time will increase the rate of reaction. The graph in Figure 31 shows the concentration of product in a reaction over time.

1 At zero time, the concentration of products is also zero as the reaction has not begun.

2 As time passes, the concentration of product increases. At this stage, the enzyme concentration is the limiting factor. If more enzymes are added, the reaction will have a faster rate.

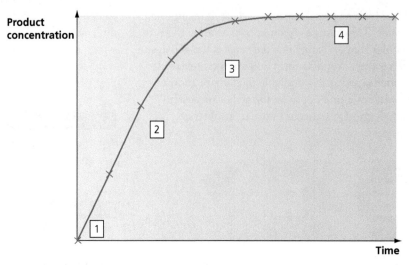

Figure 31 Change in product concentration over time

3   The reaction begins to slow down. This is because most of the substrate has been converted into the product. The substrate is running out and there is therefore less chance of a successful collision between a substrate molecule and an active site. At this point, the substrate concentration is the limiting factor in the reaction.

4   The concentration of product levels out and remains constant. All the substrate has been converted into product and the reaction has stopped.

The same reaction can be illustrated by a substrate concentration over time graph, as shown in Figure 32.

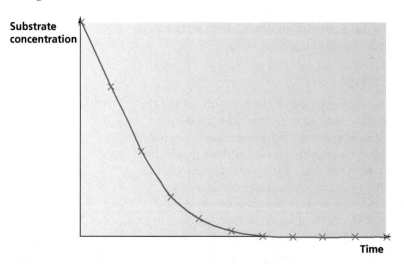

Figure 32 Change in substrate concentration over time

Again, the rate of reaction is initially high (the graph has a steep gradient) and is limited by the enzyme concentration. The rate of reaction then slows as most of the substrate is converted into product. At the end of the reaction, the substrate concentration is zero as it has all been converted to product.

> **Exam tip**
>
> When describing the point at which all the active sites are full all the time, we can say that the graph has levelled off or plateaued.

> **Exam tip**
>
> There are many different mathematical skills that could be tested in an enzyme-based question. You should ensure you are comfortable in deriving units, calculating rates, using a slope of a tangent to a curve as a measure of rate of change and understand that $y = mx + c$ represents a linear relationship.

The use of a control is important in enzyme investigations. A control shows that it is the enzymes that are causing the effect that you are measuring (the dependent variable). The usual control in an enzyme reaction is to boil and cool the enzyme solution. This denatures the enzymes and ensures that they will not catalyse any reactions. The experiment should then be repeated using the boiled and cooled enzyme solution. If the same results are obtained, this indicates that some other factor is influencing the results, not just the enzyme action.

As well as understanding the general effects of an enzyme, you also need to learn how the rate of an enzyme-controlled reaction is influenced by the following:

- temperature
- pH
- substrate concentration
- enzyme concentration
- enzyme inhibitors

Exam tip

Students often score poorly on exam questions based on the graphs shown here. Don't just learn the general shapes — ensure you fully understand what is happening at each stage of the graphs.

Temperature

Enzyme action is affected by temperature. Figure 33 shows the effect of increasing temperature on the rate of an enzyme-catalysed reaction.

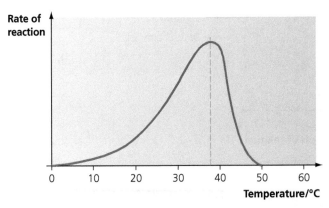

Figure 33 The effect of temperature on enzyme activity

At low temperatures the enzyme and the substrate have a low kinetic energy, which reduces the rate at which the molecules move within a solution. This means that there are fewer successful collisions between active sites and substrate molecules. Fewer enzyme–substrate complexes are formed and therefore fewer products are formed per unit time. This means that the rate of reaction is low at lower temperatures.

As the temperature increases, the enzyme and the substrate gain more kinetic energy. This increases the rate of movement of molecules within the solution, increasing the chance of successful collisions between active sites and substrate molecules. This leads to the formation of more products per unit time. Therefore, the rate of reaction increases.

The rate of reaction continues to increase as the temperature increases, until the enzyme's optimum temperature is reached. At the optimum temperature, the rate of reaction is at its highest. Higher than the optimum temperature and the rate of reaction decreases rapidly. This is because the enzyme's active sites become denatured. The hydrogen bonds holding the enzyme's tertiary structure in place break, which causes the active site to change shape. Therefore, the substrate can no longer bind with the enzyme, so no enzyme–substrate complexes are formed and so no products are formed.

As the temperature continues to increase, more active sites denature. The rate of reaction continues to fall until all the active sites have denatured and the reaction stops.

Different enzymes have different optimum temperatures. Most human enzymes have optimum temperatures just below body temperature. This ensures that a small increase in the body's temperature does not denature the enzymes.

pH

As well as having an optimum temperature, enzymes also have an optimum pH. Figure 34 shows the effect of pH on the rate of reaction of two enzymes: pepsin and amylase.

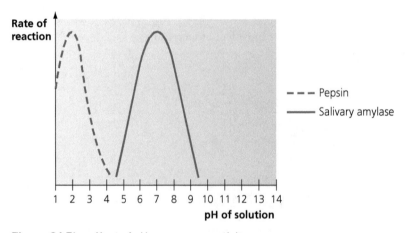

Figure 34 The effect of pH on enzyme activity

The rate of the enzyme-catalysed reaction is highest at the optimum pH. If the pH of the solution either increases or decreases from the optimum, the rate of reaction falls:

■ A small change from the optimum can cause the enzyme to become temporarily inactivated. This is only a temporary change, so if the enzyme is returned to its optimum pH it will again work as normal.

■ A large change from the optimum causes the enzyme's tertiary structure to change, altering the shape of the active site and resulting in the enzyme becoming permanently denatured.

As can be seen from Figure 34, different enzymes have a different optimum pH. Salivary amylase, a digestive enzyme found in saliva, has a slightly alkaline optimum pH, whereas pepsin, a digestive enzyme found in the stomach, has an optimum pH of 2. This allows it to maintain its maximum rate of reaction in the acidic conditions found in the stomach.

Enzymes are sensitive to pH, so when carrying out an enzyme investigation it is important to ensure that the pH remains constant. A pH buffer can be used to do this.

Exam tip

The enzymes in a reaction don't all denature immediately the temperature is higher than the optimum temperature. As the temperature increases, so increasing numbers of enzyme molecules will denature, and so the rate of reaction will fall as less enzyme is available.

Exam tip

Note that the shapes for the temperature curve and the pH curve are different. The gradient of the pH curve is the same shape either side of the optimum because decreasing or increasing the pH has the same effect. The effect of high temperature is much more pronounced as the enzyme begins to denature soon after the optimum temperature.

Knowledge check 28

Why does pepsin have a much lower optimum pH than amylase?

Substrate concentration

The concentration of the substrate also influences the rate of an enzyme-controlled reaction, as shown in Figure 35. As substrate concentration increases, the rate of reaction also increases. This is because the presence of more substrate molecules increases the chance of successful collisions between the active site and the substrate. The rate of reaction continues to increase as substrate concentration increases, until a maximum rate of reaction is reached when further increases in substrate concentration no longer increase the rate of reaction.

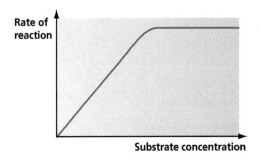

Figure 35 The effect of substrate concentration on enzyme activity

Exam tip

The graph showing the effect of increasing substrate concentration (Figure 35) is the same shape as the graph showing the change in concentration of product over time (Figure 31). When they come up in exam questions, students often confuse these two graphs. Make sure you recognise that they are showing entirely different things.

A maximum rate of reaction is reached because there is a finite concentration of enzymes. At this point, all the active sites of the enzymes are full all the time, so the maximum possible number of successful collisions is occurring. This means that there can be no increase in product formed per unit time. As it is the enzymes that are preventing the rate of reaction from increasing further, we can say that the enzyme concentration is the limiting factor. This maximum rate of reaction can be increased if the concentration of enzymes is increased. This addition of enzymes increases the number of available active sites. The rate of reaction would again continue to increase as substrate concentration increases. However, eventually the concentration of enzymes would become the limiting factor once again.

Knowledge check 29

Why does the graph in Figure 35 level off?

Enzyme concentration

Enzyme concentration also affects the rate of an enzyme reaction, as shown in Figure 36. As the enzyme concentration increases, the rate of reaction also increases. This relationship occurs only if the substrate is in excess. This means that there is always enough substrate available to fill all the available active sites. This ensures that the substrate concentration is not a limiting factor for the rate of reaction. If the substrate is not in excess, a maximum rate of reaction is reached and the graph levels off.

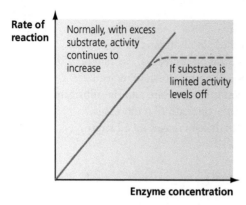

Figure 36 The effect of enzyme concentration on enzyme activity

Enzyme inhibitors

There are two types of **inhibitors**: competitive and non-competitive.

Competitive inhibitors have a similar shape to the substrate molecule of an enzyme. This allows them to enter the active site of the enzyme and prevent the actual substrate binding. As the substrate cannot bind, enzyme–substrate complexes cannot form, products are not formed and therefore the rate of reaction is not as high as it would be if the inhibitor were not present. An example of a competitive inhibitor is malonic acid. Figure 37 illustrates the action of a competitive inhibitor.

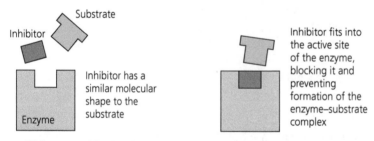

Figure 37 A competitive inhibitor competes with the substrate for the active site

Non-competitive inhibitors bind to an area of an enzyme other than the active site (e.g. an allosteric site). The inhibitor binding causes the active site of the enzyme to change shape. This means that the original substrate molecule can no longer bind to the active site. Examples of non-competitive inhibitors include cyanide and mercury. Figure 38 illustrates the action of a non-competitive inhibitor.

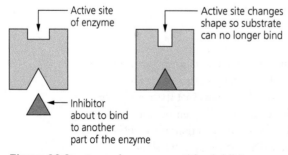

Figure 38 One type of non-competitive inhibitor

Inhibitors Molecules that reduce the ability of an enzyme to speed up a reaction.

Exam tip

Enzyme inhibition can be reversible or irreversible.

Figure 39 shows the effect of increasing substrate concentration on an enzyme-controlled reaction in the presence of a competitive inhibitor and a non-competitive inhibitor compared with no inhibitor.

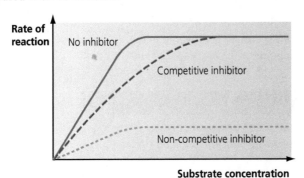

Figure 39 The effect of substrate concentration on enzyme activity in the presence of a competitive inhibitor and a non-competitive inhibitor

As can be seen from Figure 39, the effect of a competitive inhibitor can be counteracted by increasing the substrate concentration. As the substrate concentration increases, the chance of a successful substrate and active site collision becomes much greater than the chance of an inhibitor and active site collision. Therefore, as the substrate concentration increases the relative effect of the inhibitor is reduced. Eventually, if the substrate concentration is high enough, the competitive inhibitor is no longer able to affect the rate of reaction and the original theoretical maximum rate of reaction is reached.

As in the presence of a competitive inhibitor, increasing the substrate's concentration counteracts the effect of a non-competitive inhibitor and leads to the rate of reaction rising. However, the rate of reaction never reaches the maximum, no-inhibitor-present, level. This is because the non-competitive inhibitor reduces the number of available active sites in the reaction. Therefore, no matter how much the substrate concentration is increased, the rate of reaction never reaches its maximum.

Immobilised enzymes

Enzymes can be useful in industrial processes, but some of their properties can make them inefficient to use. To overcome this problem, the enzymes can be immobilised, which means that they are fixed to an inert support or trapped in a matrix. Examples of supports include alginate beads and gel membranes.

Immobilising enzymes has several advantages:
- The enzymes are more stable at higher temperatures and a wider range of pH values.
- The enzymes can be added or removed easily. This can be helpful in controlling the reaction and avoids contamination, ensuring that a pure product is formed. It also means that the enzymes can be recovered easily from the product, allowing them to be reused in the industrial process.
- A mixture of enzymes with different optimum pH and temperatures can be used together.

Knowledge check 30

How does the action of a competitive inhibitor differ from the action of a non-competitive inhibitor?

Exam tip

The concepts illustrated in Figure 39 are difficult to understand. The key point to realise is that the non-competitive inhibitor reduces the number of active sites. As the number of active sites is the rate-determining factor at high substrate concentrations, a reduction in active sites reduces the maximum rate of reaction.

Immobilised enzymes Enzymes that are bound to inert supports or trapped in a matrix.

Exam tip

When answering questions on immobilised enzymes, it is important to not just say that they 'can be reused' as an advantage. Enzymes are biological catalysts, so they can all be reused, whether immobilised or not. The key advantage to immobilised enzymes is that they can be removed easily from the reaction solution in order to be reused.

Practical work

- *Investigation into the effect of temperature or pH on enzyme activity.*
- *Investigation into the effect of enzyme or substrate concentration on enzyme activity.*

All the specified enzyme practicals are covered in the main text of this chapter. The key to answering any exam questions on them is to ensure that you can explain, using all the key terms, what is happening at any point in the reaction. You should also ensure that you can calculate rates of reaction and correctly derive their units.

Summary

After studying this topic, you should be able to:
- describe enzymes as biological catalysts that lower the activation energy of a reaction and are unchanged at the end of it
- explain the action of an enzyme and relate its specificity to the tertiary structure of its active site
- explain the differences between the lock and key and the induced-fit theories of enzyme action
- interpret graphs of enzyme-catalysed reactions showing the change of product or substrate over time
- interpret graphs showing the effects of temperature, pH, substrate concentration and enzyme concentration on rate of reaction
- explain the effects of temperature, pH, substrate concentration and enzyme concentration using collision theory
- explain the action of competitive and non-competitive inhibitors and interpret graphs showing the effect of increasing substrate concentration on rate of reaction when inhibitors are present
- describe the importance of a control experiment and the use of pH buffers in enzyme investigations
- explain the advantages of immobilising enzymes

Nucleic acids and their function

DNA and RNA are nucleic acids. **Deoxyribonucleic acid (DNA)** is the molecule that carries an organism's genetic code. The main function of DNA is replication and providing the code for protein synthesis. DNA replication ensures that the DNA is copied accurately for cell division. When a cell divides, a copy of the DNA is passed to both daughter cells. **Ribonucleic acid (RNA)** is another nucleic acid that is involved in the synthesis of proteins. **Adenosine triphosphate (ATP)** is a nucleotide found in all living cells and is involved in the transfer of energy.

The structure of nucleotides

Nucleotides are the monomers from which nucleic acids like DNA and RNA are made. Nucleotides are made up of three components (see Figure 40):

- a phosphate group
- a pentose (five-carbon) sugar — in DNA, the pentose sugar is deoxyribose and in RNA and ATP it is ribose
- an organic nitrogenous base

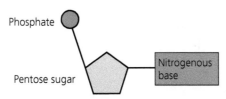

Figure 40 All nucleotides have the same structure. The phosphate is attached to the fifth carbon atom in the sugar

ATP

ATP is known as the universal energy currency as it is used in all energy-requiring reactions in all cells in all living organisms. It can diffuse easily across membranes and cannot be stored. ATP comprises adenine (a nitrogenous base) joined to ribose (a five-carbon sugar) and three phosphate groups (Figure 41).

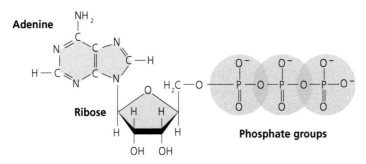

Figure 41 The structure of ATP

Nucleic acids Polymers of nucleotides, for example DNA and RNA.

Exam tip

It is okay to use DNA and RNA as abbreviations in exam answers.

Nucleotide The basic unit from which nucleic acids are formed. They are a combination of phosphate, a pentose sugar and an organic base.

ATP is used in many energy-requiring reactions, such as:

■ active transport
■ protein synthesis
■ nerve transmission
■ muscle contraction

ATP is formed by the addition of phosphate (phosphorylation) to **adenosine diphosphate (ADP)**. This is a condensation reaction. When hydrolysis occurs, the terminal phosphate bond is broken and 30.6 kJ mol of energy is released (Figure 42).

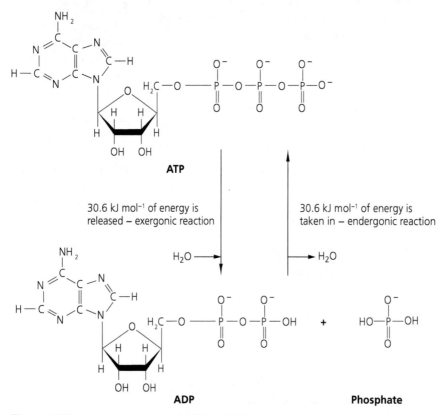

Figure 42 The interconversion of ATP and ADP

The structure of nucleic acids

Pyrimidine and purine bases

There are five different nitrogenous bases. They can be divided into two groups: pyrimidine bases and purine bases. Pyrimidine bases have a single-ring structure, whereas purine bases have a double-ring structure. Figure 43 illustrates the different single- and double-ring structures of pyrimidine and purine bases.

■ Pyrimidine bases — single-ring structure:
  – cytosine (C)
  – thymine (T)
  – uracil (U)

- Purine bases — double-ring structure:
  - adenine (A)
  - guanine (G)

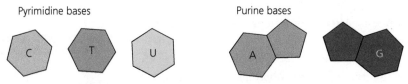

Figure 43 The different structures of pyrimidine and purine bases

Cytosine, thymine, adenine and guanine are found in DNA. Cytosine, uracil, adenine and guanine are found in RNA.

DNA

DNA is made up of two strands of nucleotides (Figure 44) wound into a double helix. The deoxyribose of one nucleotide forms a bond with the phosphate of another nucleotide to form a **sugar–phosphate backbone**. The two strands of the double helix are held together by hydrogen bonds between pairs of nitrogenous bases. A purine base pairs with a pyrimidine base:

- Adenine always pairs with thymine. Two hydrogen bonds form between adenine and thymine.
- Cytosine always pairs with guanine. Three hydrogen bonds form between cytosine and guanine.

This is known as **complementary base pairing** and is important in ensuring that DNA replicates correctly. It also means that there is the same proportion of adenine and thymine in a DNA molecule and the same proportion of cytosine and guanine. In DNA the polynucleotide strands are antiparallel (5′ end to 3′ end and 3′ end to 5′ end.)

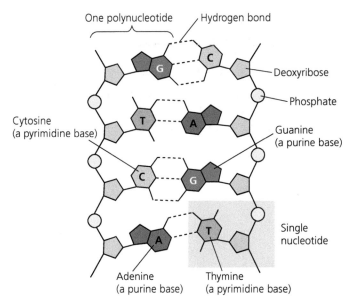

Figure 44 The molecular structure of DNA

Exam tip

Look out for the single- or double-ring structures of bases in DNA diagrams. It may help you to identify the base.

Knowledge check 31

What are the purine bases?

Knowledge check 32

What forms the backbone of a DNA strand?

Exam tip

When answering questions about the structure of DNA, try to use the key term **complementary base pairing**. Don't abbreviate the bases to their first letters — use their full names.

RNA

Unlike DNA, RNA is usually single-stranded. There are three different types of RNA:

- **messenger RNA (mRNA)** is formed in the nucleus by transcription of a strand of DNA. mRNA carries the code for the polypeptide chain that will be formed in the translation stage of protein synthesis. After it has formed, the mRNA leaves the nucleus through the nuclear pore
- **ribosomal RNA (rRNA)** combines with protein to form ribosomes
- **transfer RNA (tRNA)** transports amino acids to the ribosome for translation. tRNA has an anticodon and an amino attachment site

Knowledge check 33

Where is mRNA formed?

Semi-conservative DNA replication

DNA carries the genetic code for an organism. The genetic code is the code for protein synthesis and it is therefore fundamental to the life of any organism.

Genetic stability is also important to an organism. It relies on the genetic code being passed on to daughter cells without changes or errors. Mutations are rarely beneficial and can lead to the production of non-functional cells or, in the worst case, could threaten the survival of the whole organism. An example is a mutation that leads to the activation of an oncogene and the onset of cancer. To ensure that this does not occur and genetic stability is preserved, it is important that DNA is replicated accurately. The process of DNA replication is outlined below.

1   One double-stranded molecule of DNA unwinds and the hydrogen bonds holding the two strands together are broken by the enzyme DNA helicase. This process is sometimes referred to as unzipping.

2   The enzyme DNA polymerase catalyses the addition of free DNA nucleotides to form two new complementary strands (adenine bonding with thymine and cytosine bonding with guanine) using both original strands as templates.

3   Hydrogen bonds form between each pair of complementary DNA strands (one original strand, one new strand), causing each new molecule to twist to form a double helix. This produces two molecules of DNA that are identical to each other and to the original DNA molecule.

DNA replication is **semi-conservative** (Figure 45). This means that each new DNA molecule contains one original strand and one newly formed strand. This was shown experimentally by Meselson and Stahl. Their experiment is detailed below.

Genetic code The way in which information about the sequence of amino acids in a protein is coded by the bases on a molecule of DNA.

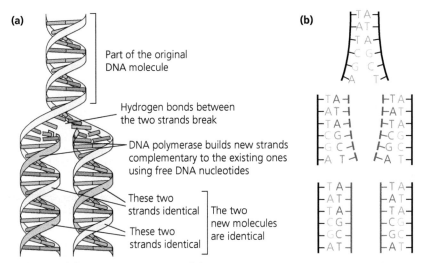

Figure 45 (a) DNA replication and (b) semi-conservative replication of DNA

Meselson and Stahl's work

Meselson and Stahl cultivated some bacteria in a flask that contained a nutrient medium whose only source of nitrogen was ^{15}N (a heavier isotope than the more common ^{14}N). The bacteria took up the nitrogen and used it to form the nitrogenous bases of nucleotides. After many generations, all the nitrogenous bases in the bacterial DNA therefore contained the heavier ^{15}N. When these bacteria were lysed (broken open) and centrifuged, the DNA settled at a low point in the centrifuge tube. The position at the end of the centrifugation relates to the density of the molecule. As this DNA contained ^{15}N, it was denser than DNA that contained ^{14}N. It therefore settled at a relatively low point in the tube.

The scientists then allowed the bacteria to divide once in a medium containing ^{14}N (the lighter isotope). Once again, the bacteria were lysed and centrifuged. The DNA now settled at a midway point in the tube, indicating that it was less dense than the DNA in the first generation. This is because all the bacterial cells now contained 'hybrid' DNA. Hybrid DNA is DNA that contains one original ^{15}N-containing strand and a newly formed strand that contained ^{14}N in its nitrogenous bases. This result proved that DNA replication was not conservative. Conservative replication theory suggested that the original double stranded DNA molecule remained and a totally new double-stranded molecule was produced. By forming hybrid DNA, Meselson and Stahl proved this to be incorrect.

However, the result could be explained either by semi-conservative replication (one original strand and one new strand) or by dispersive replication (both strands consist of sections of new and old DNA). In order to prove that the DNA had been semi-conservatively replicated, they allowed the bacteria to divide a second time on the ^{14}N growth medium. When Meselson and Stahl extracted the DNA and centrifuged it, a hybrid band again formed at a midway point up the tube. However, another band of less dense DNA containing only ^{14}N formed further up the tube. This result proved that the DNA was semi-conservatively replicated. Meselson and Stahl's investigation is shown in Figure 46.

Exam tip

Questions on Meselson and Stahl are quite common and this topic is fairly complex, so make sure you have learned it thoroughly.

Knowledge check 34

Why is DNA replication said to be semi-conservative?

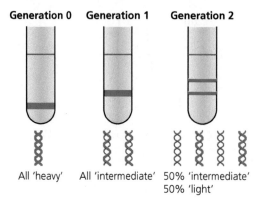

Figure 46 Meselson and Stahl's experiment

Protein synthesis

Proteins are of vital importance in cells. The code for the structure of proteins is carried in the cell's DNA. During protein synthesis, this code is 'read' and the amino acids are arranged in the correct sequence to form the protein. The sequence of nucleotide bases that codes for one polypeptide is a **gene**. Each amino acid is coded for by three nucleotide bases known as **triplets** and the three bases that code for an amino acid are a **codon**. As there are 20 amino acids and 64 possible codons (the number of combinations of the four different nucleotide bases in DNA in a group of three), each amino acid has more than one codon that codes for it. There are also stop and start codons that are used to control protein synthesis. The codons and the amino acids they code for are shown in Figure 47.

Knowledge check 35

What is the section of DNA that codes for one polypeptide called?

Exam tip

You don't have to learn this codon table but you should be able to use it if it appears in a question.

Second position

		U	C	A	G	
First position (5′ end)	U	UUU ⎤ Phe UUC ⎦ UUA ⎤ Leu UUG ⎦	UCU ⎤ UCC ⎥ Ser UCA ⎥ UCG ⎦	UAU ⎤ Tyr UAC ⎦ UAA stop UAG stop	UGU ⎤ Cys UGC ⎦ UGA stop UGG Trp	U C A G
	C	CUU ⎤ CUC ⎥ Leu CUA ⎥ CUG ⎦	CCU ⎤ CCC ⎥ Pro CCA ⎥ CCG ⎦	CAU ⎤ His CAC ⎦ CAA ⎤ Gln CAG ⎦	CGU ⎤ CGC ⎥ Arg CGA ⎥ CGG ⎦	U C A G
	A	AUU ⎤ Ile AUC ⎥ AUA ⎦ AUG Met	ACU ⎤ ACC ⎥ Thr ACA ⎥ ACG ⎦	AAU ⎤ Asn AAC ⎦ AAA ⎤ Lys AAG ⎦	AGU ⎤ Ser AGC ⎦ AGA ⎤ Arg AGG ⎦	U C A G
	G	GUU ⎤ GUC ⎥ Val GUA ⎥ GUG ⎦	GCU ⎤ GCC ⎥ Ala GCA ⎥ GCG ⎦	GAU ⎤ Asp GAC ⎦ GAA ⎤ Glu GAG ⎦	GGU ⎤ GGC ⎥ Gly GGA ⎥ GGG ⎦	U C A G

Third position (3′ end)

Figure 47 RNA codons

The regions of the DNA that contain the code for proteins are called **exons**. The non-coding DNA between the exons are known as **introns**. There are two stages to protein synthesis: transcription and translation. Prokaryotic genes are usually continuous genes without non-coding sections.

Transcription

Transcription occurs in the nucleus. One of the DNA strands acts as a template (known as the anti-sense strand). The process of transcription is detailed below.

1 A section of the DNA unwinds and the hydrogen bonds holding the two strands of the DNA break (the DNA unzips).

2 The enzyme RNA polymerase catalyses the addition of free RNA nucleotides to form a complementary strand of mRNA. The bases of the RNA are joined to produce a complete single-stranded molecule. Thymine, cytosine and guanine on the DNA molecule pair with adenine, guanine and cytosine respectively on the mRNA strand. However, unlike in DNA replication, adenine bases on the DNA strand are complementary to uracil bases on the mRNA strand (thymine is not found in RNA).

3 When transcription is complete, the hydrogen bonds between the two strands of DNA reform.

4 The mRNA formed is known as pre-mRNA. The exons are removed from the pre-mRNA to form functional mRNA.

5 The mRNA molecule then leaves the nucleus through the nuclear pore and travels to a ribosome in the cytoplasm.

The process of transcription is shown in Figure 48.

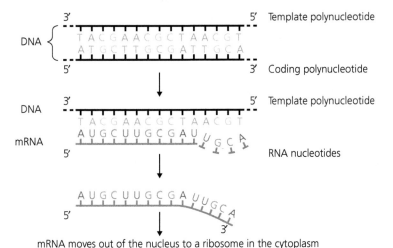

mRNA moves out of the nucleus to a ribosome in the cytoplasm

Figure 48 Transcription

Transcription The conversion of the genetic code to a sequence of nucleotides in mRNA.

Knowledge check 36

Where does transcription occur?

Knowledge check 37

Which DNA strand acts as a template for the formation of a strand of mRNA?

Knowledge check 38

How does the mRNA travel from the nucleus to the cytoplasm?

Translation

The purpose of transcription is to transfer the code for the polypeptide from DNA to mRNA so it can be transported to the ribosome. In the next stage, translation, this code is used to form the polypeptide. In translation, tRNA is used to transfer amino acids to the ribosome.

The anticodon on the tRNA molecule determines the specific amino acid that the tRNA transfers — it is complementary to the codon for that amino acid on the mRNA. The specific amino acid joins to the amino acid attachment site on the tRNA molecule. This process is known as activation and requires ATP. The structure of a tRNA molecule and activation are shown in Figure 49.

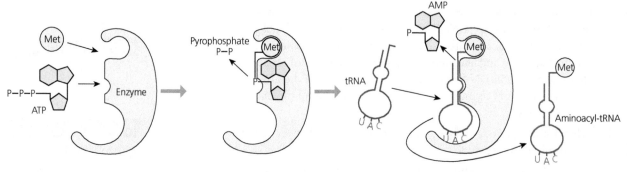

Figure 49 The enzyme shown here only accepts methionine and its specific tRNA molecule

Translation occurs at the ribosome. The two subunits of the ribosome fit around the mRNA and the mRNA now sits in the mRNA groove.

1   The large subunit of the ribosome has two binding sites on it. This means that two tRNA molecules can bind with the ribosome at any one time.

2   The two amino acids carried by the tRNA are connected by a peptide bond formed by a condensation reaction that is catalysed by a ribosomal enzyme.

3   The first tRNA molecule leaves the ribosome and the second tRNA moves along to take its place.

4   Another tRNA with the next amino acid in the sequence can then fill the vacant binding site.

5   The codon on the mRNA is complementary to the anticodon on the newly arrived tRNA molecule. They briefly form a codon–anticodon complex.

6   The ribosome moves along the mRNA reading each codon, and the specific amino acid is added to the growing polypeptide chain. Translation stops when a stop codon is reached. At this point the two subunits of the ribosome separate and the polypeptide chain leaves the ribosome.

The process of translation is shown in Figure 50.

After translation has finished, the polypeptide chain can be further modified in the Golgi body. From here, secretory proteins are budded off in vesicles. They then travel to the cell's plasma membrane, the vesicle fuses with the plasma membrane and the protein is released from the cell by **exocytosis**.

> **Exam tip**
>
> A common mistake is to mix up what occurs in transcription and in translation. Make sure you are clear on the locations, enzymes involved and products formed at each of the stages.

> Translation The conversion of the code in mRNA to a sequence of amino acids.

> **Knowledge check 39**
>
> Where does translation occur?

> **Knowledge check 40**
>
> What part of the tRNA molecule is complementary to the codon on the mRNA?

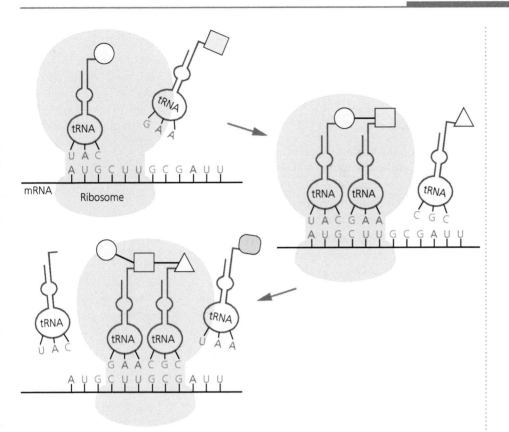

Figure 50 Translation

Practical work

■ *Simple extraction of DNA from living material.*

This is a straightforward practical that allows you to observe DNA extracted from cells.

Summary

After studying this topic, you should be able to:
■ describe the structure of a nucleotide and its components
■ explain that nucleotides form the nucleic acids DNA and RNA
■ describe the structure of ATP
■ understand the role of ATP as an energy carrier molecule
■ describe the structural differences between DNA and RNA

■ describe the functions of DNA as replication in dividing cells and carrying the code for protein synthesis
■ describe the structures and functions of mRNA and tRNA
■ explain the concept of semi-conservative replication and the work of Meselson and Stahl
■ describe the processes of transcription and translation
■ understand the concept of complementary base pairing and use it to describe the structure of DNA

Genetic information is copied and passed on to daughter cells

Cell division is the process whereby a cell splits to form daughter cells. There are two types of cell division: mitosis and meiosis. Although mitosis and meiosis both produce new daughter cells, the characteristics of these daughter cells are quite different:

- **Mitosis** produces two diploid daughter cells that are genetically identical to each other and to the parent cell. This provides genetic stability.
- **Meiosis** produces four haploid daughter cells that are genetically different to each other and to the original parent cell. The daughter cells formed in meiosis are used to produce **gametes** — sex cells used for sexual reproduction. These cells contain one chromosome from each pair of homologous chromosomes.

Chromosomes

One of the most important aspects of cell division is the behaviour of the chromosomes. A chromosome consists of DNA and protein. Genes are specific sections of the DNA in chromosomes that code for one polypeptide. Each chromosome is made up of two identical chromatids joined by a centromere. Chromosomes form homologous pairs. Each chromosome in a pair contains the same genes but in different forms. Figure 51 shows a pair of homologous chromosomes.

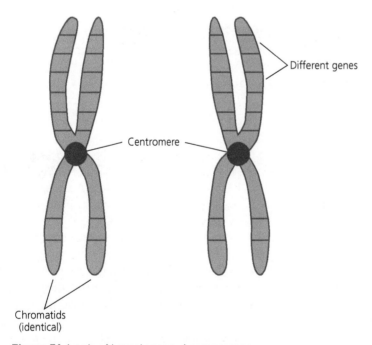

Figure 51 A pair of homologous chromosomes

Exam tip

Many similar-sounding words are used in cell division (e.g. chromosome, chromatid, centromere, centriole). Make sure you are clear about what each one means.

Chromosome Consists of a tightly coiled length of DNA, closely associated with a small amount of RNA and a number of proteins.

Homologous chromosomes A pair of chromosomes that carry matching genes, one maternal (from the mother) and one paternal (from the father).

Chromatid One of the two strands of genetic material that make up a chromosome.

Centromere The region on a chromosome that holds the sister chromatids together during the early stages of cell division.

Exam tip

Try to use the key terms 'haploid' and 'diploid' when talking about the daughter cells produced in cell division.

A cell with the full number of chromosomes is known as **diploid**. In humans, this means a cell contains 46 chromosomes forming 23 homologous pairs. A cell with only one chromosome from each homologous pair (so half the diploid number) is known as **haploid**. Human haploid cells contain 23 chromosomes. Haploid cells are used as gametes by sexually reproducing organisms. When two haploid gametes fuse during fertilisation, they form a cell that has the full diploid number of chromosomes. Different organisms have different numbers of chromosomes, for example cows have 60 chromosomes whereas dogs have 78.

The cell cycle and mitosis

The cell cycle is shown in Figure 52. When a cell is not undergoing cell division, it is in **interphase**. During interphase, the following processes occur:

- DNA replicates
- protein synthesis occurs
- ATP is synthesised
- organelles are produced

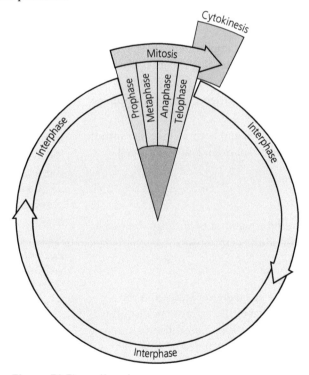

Figure 52 The cell cycle

At the end of interphase, mitosis occurs. This can be divided into four stages: **prophase**, **metaphase**, **anaphase** and **telophase** (Figure 53). It is important to understand that mitosis is a continuous process and we divide it up into separate stages to aid our understanding of it.

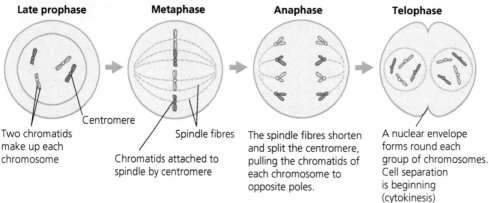

Figure 53 The stages of mitosis

Mitosis is essential for the growth of organisms, the repair of damaged tissues and the replacement of dead cells. In some organisms, it is also used for **asexual reproduction**. Uncontrolled cell division leads to the growth of cancerous tumours.

Tumour An abnormal mass of tissues.

Prophase

This is the longest stage of mitosis. This means that in a sample of cells undergoing mitosis, a large number of cells will be in prophase. The following events occur during this stage:

- The chromatin, which is free in the nucleus, condenses to form the chromosomes (two chromatids joined at the centromere).
- The centrioles move to the poles (either end) of the cell and begin to form the **spindle fibres**. The spindle is a web of protein microtubules that extends across the cell.
- The nuclear membrane breaks down.

Metaphase

During metaphase, the chromosomes line up at the equator of the cell (in the middle) and the spindle fibres attach to the chromosomes at the centromere.

Anaphase

During anaphase, the spindle fibres contract, the centromere separates and the chromatids (now called sister chromosomes) are pulled to the opposite poles of the cell. Anaphase is the fastest stage of mitosis. This means that if you observe a sample of cells undergoing mitosis, you will see very few cells in the anaphase stage.

Telophase

During telophase, the chromosomes unwind back to chromatin. The nuclear envelope reforms and the spindle breaks down.

Cytokinesis

At the end of telophase, the cell divides by **cytokinesis** to form two genetically identical daughter cells. In animal cells, this is done by a 'pinching in' of the plasma membrane. In plant cells, a cell plate forms between the dividing cells. This then forms the new cell wall of the two cells.

Exam tip

Remembering the correct order of the stages of mitosis is fundamental to understanding and explaining mitosis, but students often mix them up. A mnemonic can be a good way of remembering the order, such as Paul Makes Awful Toast (prophase, metaphase, anaphase, telophase).

Exam tip

When drawing a cell undergoing anaphase, it is important to draw the chromosomes as V shapes, with the point of the V (and the point of spindle attachment) facing the pole of the cell it is being pulled towards.

Meiosis

Meiosis is a form of cell division that is used to produce gametes (sex cells) in most sexually reproducing organisms. Four haploid (containing half the number of chromosomes of an ordinary diploid body cell) daughter cells are produced, which are genetically different from each other and from the original cell. As the male and females gametes produced are haploid, when they fuse during fertilisation the zygote formed has the full diploid number of chromosomes. As each gamete is genetically different from each other and from the parent cell, meiosis also introduces genetic variation into sexual reproduction.

Meiosis has two stages, **meiosis I** and **meiosis II**. As in mitosis, each of these stages can be further divided into prophase, metaphase, anaphase and telophase. The process of meiosis is shown in Figure 54.

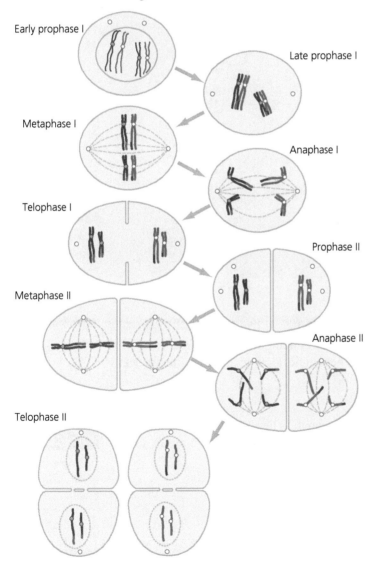

Figure 54 Meiosis to form sperm cells in an animal that has a diploid number of 4. Maternal chromosomes are blue, paternal chromosomes are red

> **Exam tip**
>
> You must be able to describe and draw all the stages of mitosis. If you are asked to draw one or more of the stages, you will often be given a number of chromosomes to include, so make sure you stick to this number.

> **Exam tip**
>
> It is important that you can describe what happens in meiosis *and* that you can draw it and recognise it on a diagram. You may also be asked to identify the stages from photographs of cells undergoing meiosis. The key to answering such questions is to look carefully at what the chromosomes are doing.

Meiosis I

Prophase I

The chromatin condenses to form the chromosomes and the nuclear membrane breaks down. Each chromosome is made up of two identical chromatids joined by the centromere. The chromosomes are arranged in their homologous pairs. The two chromosomes in a homologous pair form a **bivalent**. The chromatid's homologous chromosomes touch at points known as **chiasmata** (singular: chiasma), where **crossing over** occurs (Figure 55). This is the swapping of genes between homologous chromosomes in a bivalent. Crossing over is an important source of genetic variation in meiosis as it means that the two chromatids that make up each chromosome are no longer identical to each other. The centrioles also begin to produce the proteins for the microtubules that will form the spindle.

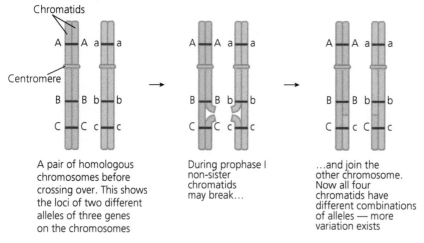

A pair of homologous chromosomes before crossing over. This shows the loci of two different alleles of three genes on the chromosomes

During prophase I non-sister chromatids may break…

…and join the other chromosome. Now all four chromatids have different combinations of alleles — more variation exists

Figure 55 Crossing over produces new combinations of alleles

Metaphase I

The bivalents arrange themselves at the equator of the cell. This arrangement is a random distribution so it leads to **independent assortment**, another important source of variation in meiosis (Figure 56). The spindle fibres attach to the centromeres of each chromosome.

Anaphase I

The spindle fibres contract and the bivalents separate. The chromosomes are pulled to the opposite poles of the cell. The chromosomes are still double structures at this point because the centromere has not split.

Telophase I

Cytokinesis occurs and two new cells are produced.

Knowledge check 43

At which points on chromosomes does crossing over occur?

Exam tip

Make sure you can fully explain the causes of variation in meiosis.

Knowledge check 44

During which stage of meiosis do the bivalents separate?

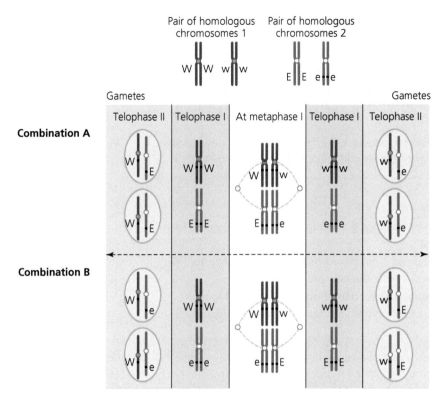

Figure 56 Independent assortment: the different arrangement of the two pairs of chromosomes during metaphase I in A and B has led to the formation of different daughter cells

Meiosis II

The events involved in meiosis II are similar to mitosis.

Prophase II

The spindle forms at right angles to the spindle used in meiosis I.

Metaphase II

The chromosomes line up at the equator. The spindle fibres attach to the centromere.

Anaphase II

The spindle fibres contract, the centromeres split and the chromosomes are pulled to the opposite poles of the cell. They are no longer double structures.

Telophase II

The chromosomes uncoil to form chromatin and the nuclear envelope reforms. Cytokinesis occurs and each cell produces two cells.

Practical work

■ *Scientific drawing of cells from slides of root tip to show stages of mitosis.*

You should be able to identify the stages of mitosis from photos of root tip cells — remember to look where the chromosomes are and how they are behaving.

■ *Scientific drawing of cells from prepared slides of developing anthers to show stages of meiosis.*

Make sure you can identify stages from photographs. You should also know that the anther is a site of meiosis in flowering plants and mitosis occurs at the root tips.

The sources of variation in meiosis are:

■ **crossing over** — during prophase I homologous chromosomes in a bivalent swap genes at points called chiasmata

■ **independent assortment** — during metaphase I homologous chromosomes in bivalents arrange themselves randomly at the equator

■ **mixing of parental chromosomes at fertilisation** — at fertilisation the chromosomes of both parents (the genotypes) are mixed to form the diploid zygote

Summary

After studying this topic, you should be able to:

■ understand the relationship between chromatin, chromatids and homologous chromosomes

■ describe the processes that occur in interphase

■ describe the events that occur in each of the stages of mitosis

■ explain the differences between mitosis and meiosis

■ describe the events that occur in each of the stages of meiosis

■ describe the sources of genetic variation in meiosis

Questions & Answers

This section contains questions on each of the six topics in Unit 1/Component 1. They are written in the same style as the questions in the exam so they will give you an idea of the sort of thing you will be asked to do in the real exam. After each question, there are answers by two different students (student B answers are generally stronger than student A answers), followed by comments on what they have written. These are important because they give you an insight into the responses the examiners are looking for in the exam. They also highlight some of the common mistakes that students make.

Each question is followed by a brief analysis of what to watch out for when answering the question (icon ⓔ). All student responses are then followed by examiner's comments. These are preceded by the icon ⓔ and indicate where credit is due. In the weaker answers, they also point out areas for improvement, specific problems and common errors, such as lack of clarity, weak or non-existent development, irrelevance, misinterpretation of the question and mistaken meanings of terms.

In addition to sample structured questions, this section of the guide also contains an extended response question along with some advice on how best to approach extended response questions in general.

AS Unit 1/Component 1 exam

The Unit 1/Component 1 exam lasts 1 hour 30 minutes and is worth 20% of the WJEC Biology A-level and 50% of the Eduqas Biology AS level. The exam is made up of structured questions and an extended response question. The extended response question is marked in bands.

Eduqas A-Level Biology

Core Concepts can be assessed in any of the three component examinations. 'Genetic Information is copied and passed on to daughter cells' will be assessed in the Component 2 examination.

■ Chemical elements are joined together to form biological compounds

Question 1

The diagram shows two monosaccharides.

(A) 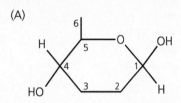   (B)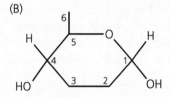

(a) Identify the two monosaccharides shown in the diagram.   (2 marks)

(b) Describe one way in which the structure of the monosaccharide found in DNA would differ from (A) and (B).   (1 mark)

(c) Describe the formation of maltose from two monosaccharides.   (4 marks)

ⓔ This is a straightforward biochemistry question but it has a couple of areas that you could find challenging. It is important to study all biochemistry diagrams carefully — it is easy to get different molecules mixed up. Part (c) carries 4 marks, so it is important to ensure you write a detailed answer that contains all the main points and key words required.

Student A

(a) (A) = β-glucose, (B) = α-glucose

ⓔ **2/2 marks awarded** Both monosaccharides are identified correctly.

(b) The monosaccharide found in DNA is deoxyribose, whereas the monosaccharides shown in the diagrams are glucose.

ⓔ **0/1 mark awarded** Student A has correctly identified the monosaccharide in DNA as deoxyribose but this is not what the question is asking — the question is asking for the differences in structure between the monosaccharides shown in the diagram and the monosaccharide in DNA. The most obvious difference in structure is that the monosaccharides shown are isomers of glucose so are hexose sugars and contain six carbon atoms; deoxyribose is a pentose sugar and so it contains five carbon atoms — explaining this would have gained the mark.

(c) Two glucose molecules join together in a condensation reaction.

ⓔ **2/4 marks awarded** Student A's answer is correct and gains 2 marks, 1 mark for saying that maltose is formed from two glucose molecules and 1 mark for correctly identifying the reaction as a condensation reaction. However, a simple one-line answer like this will not score 4 marks. Look carefully at the mark allocation of each question and ensure that you include enough detail to earn all the available marks for questions with a high mark allocation like this one.

Student B

(a) (A) = α-glucose, (B) = β-glucose

ⓔ **0/2 marks awarded** Most diagrams you will see of the two isomers of glucose will show α-glucose first and β-glucose second. However, examiners may try to catch you out by presenting things in non-standard ways to check that you have understood and thought about the work. Study all diagrams carefully — if student B had done this, they would have realised that the arrangement of the hydrogen atom and OH group on carbon 1 in diagram (A) clearly shows that it is β-glucose.

(b) The monosaccharide found in DNA is deoxyribose, which is a pentose sugar and so it has five carbon atoms. The two molecules shown are hexose sugars that contain six carbon atoms.

ⓔ **1/1 mark awarded** This is an excellent answer that gains the mark.

(c) In order to form maltose, two glucose molecules combine in a condensation reaction. The glycosidic bond in the molecule is formed between carbon 1 of one of the glucose molecules and carbon 4 of the other glucose molecule. A molecule of water is also formed.

ⓔ **4/4 marks awarded** This is a detailed answer that gets all 4 marks. Longer answer questions such as this one will often have more acceptable answers than there are marks available. For example, for this part there were five possible points and student B got all five.

Overall, student B answered this question well, but did not score full marks because of making a silly mistake in part (a).

Question 2

(a) Arginine and glycine are two different amino acids. How do arginine and glycine differ from each other? (1 mark)

The diagram shows a protein.

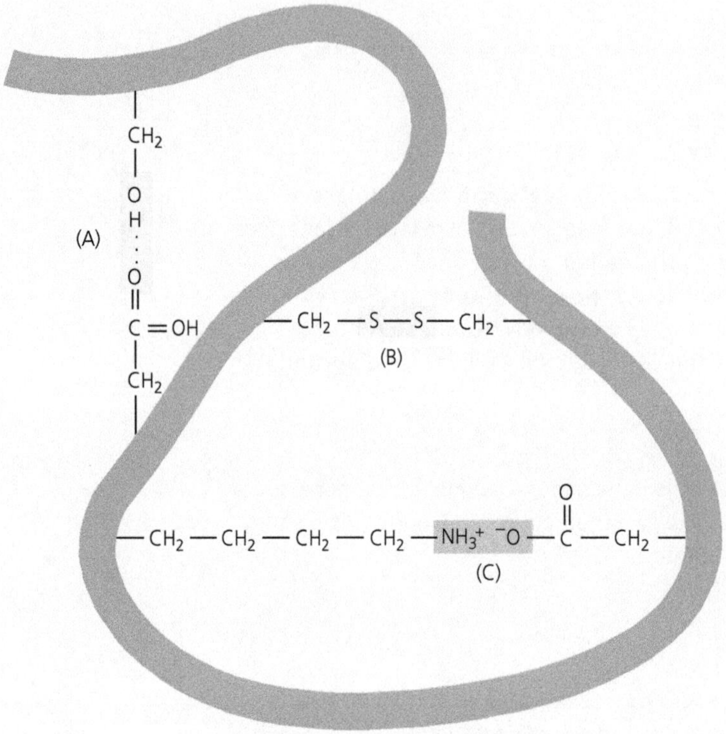

(b) (i) Label the bonds shown at (A), (B) and (C) in the diagram. (3 marks)

(ii) Is the protein in the diagram a fibrous or globular protein? Explain your answer. (3 marks)

(iii) How would a quaternary protein differ from the one shown in the diagram? (1 mark)

(c) Which biochemical test could be used to determine if a protein is present in a solution? (1 mark)

🄴 Make sure you study any diagrams in the exam paper carefully. This question asks you to specifically identify features of the diagram and to look at it as a whole to identify the class of protein shown and compare it to a quaternary protein.

Student A

(a) Different structures

🄴 **0/1 mark awarded** This answer does not contain enough detail — to be awarded the mark the student needed to mention the different R groups of the two amino acids.

(b) (i) (A) = hydrogen bonds, (B) = disulphide bridges, (C) = ionic bonds

e **3/3 marks awarded** All three bonds are correct, so this answer earns 3 marks.

(ii) The protein shown is a globular protein.

e **1/3 marks awarded** Student A has correctly identified the protein in the diagram as a globular protein, so gains 1 mark. However, they have failed to answer the second part of this question and have not explained why the protein shown is a globular protein. It is important when answering exam questions to take time to read each question fully and ensure that your answer addresses all the points asked for.

(iii) A quaternary protein would be made up of two or more polypeptides. The protein shown only has one polypeptide chain.

e **1/1 mark awarded** This is a good answer and gains the mark.

(c) Add Benedict's reagent.

e **0/1 mark awarded** The student has mixed up the biochemical test for reducing sugars and the test for protein. This is a common mistake (because they both begin with the letter B) that underlines the importance of learning the biochemical tests thoroughly.

Student B

(a) They would have different R groups.

e **1/1 mark awarded** This is the correct answer that gains the mark available.

(b) (i) (A) = hydrogen bonds, (B) = ?, (C) = ionic bonds

e **2/3 marks awarded** (A) and (C) are identified correctly, gaining 2 marks, but student B has failed to recognise the disulphide bridge (which could also have been labelled as a covalent bond). It is important that you can recall facts like all the bonds in the tertiary structure of a protein as they are a source of easy marks. Student B should have been able to identify bond (B) from the S (the chemical symbol for sulphur).

(ii) This is a globular protein. You can tell this as it has a tertiary structure. Fibrous proteins don't have a tertiary structure.

e **3/3 marks awarded** Student B has correctly identified the protein in the diagram as a globular protein and explained the structural features that distinguish it from a fibrous protein.

> **(iii)** A quaternary protein would be haemoglobin.

e **0/1 mark awarded** Student B has given an example of a quaternary protein without describing how it differs from the protein in the diagram, so does not get the mark.

> **(c)** The biuret test.

e **1/1 mark awarded** Student B has correctly identified the biochemical test for proteins and so gains the mark.

Question 3

A student was given four solutions labelled A, B, C and D. She knew that the solutions contained:

- glucose
- starch
- an enzyme that breaks down starch into glucose
- sucrose

The diagram shows the test method she carried out.

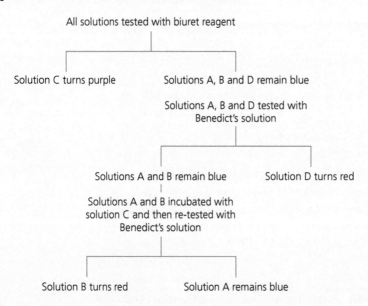

All solutions tested with biuret reagent

Solution C turns purple   Solutions A, B and D remain blue

Solutions A, B and D tested with Benedict's solution

Solutions A and B remain blue   Solution D turns red

Solutions A and B incubated with solution C and then re-tested with Benedict's solution

Solution B turns red   Solution A remains blue

(a) Identify the solutions A–D. (4 marks)

(b) Explain why solutions A and B gave different results when heated with Benedict's solution after they had been incubated with tube C. (3 marks)

ⓔ This question is quite challenging. It is important to take your time and follow the experimental process through carefully. It may be helpful to write on the diagram when you think you have identified one of the solutions and then tick off that word in the stem of the question. Once you think you have worked out what each solution is, go back through the question and ensure that there is no evidence that contradicts your assumptions.

Student A

(a) A = glucose, B = starch, C = enzyme, D = sucrose

ⓔ **2/4 marks awarded** The student correctly identifies solutions B and C but has mixed up solutions A and D, so only scores 2 of the 4 marks available.

(b) The starch in solution B is broken down by the enzyme in solution C, the glucose produced then gives a positive result to being heated with Benedict's solution.

ⓔ **1/3 marks awarded** This answer is not explained well, but it is a good example of how you can still get some marks from a question even if you do not fully understand it. Student A has used their answer in part (a) and the information in the stem of the question to gain 1 mark out of the possible 3 available by stating the effect of the enzyme. If student A had read back over the question and applied the logic of their answer in part (b) to their answer in part (a), they would have realised the mistake made (glucose would have given a positive result to the Benedict's test) and could have scored an extra 2 marks. This underlines the importance of always reading back over the answers you have written in an exam.

Student B

(a) A = sucrose, B = starch, C = enzyme, D = glucose

ⓔ **4/4 marks awarded** All the solutions are correctly identified, scoring all 4 marks.

(b) The enzyme in tube C breaks down the starch into glucose. The glucose produced then gives a positive result to being heated with Benedict's solution. As glucose is a reducing sugar, it forms a brick-red precipitate. Sucrose is not broken down by the enzyme and as it is a non-reducing sugar it does not form a brick-red precipitate when heated with Benedict's solution.

ⓔ **3/3 marks awarded** This is an excellent answer that fully explains the reasoning behind the different results of solutions A and B. It scores the maximum 3 marks for describing the effect of the enzyme; identifying the products of the enzyme reaction as being reducing sugars and so producing a positive result when heated with Benedict's solution; stating the fact that as sucrose is a non-reducing sugar it gives a negative result when heated with Benedict's solution.

■Cell structure and organisation

Question 4

The diagram shows a prokaryotic cell.

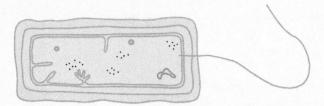

(a) Describe three features shown in the diagram that allow you to identify the cell as a prokaryote.   (3 marks)

(b) How would the cell wall in the above organism differ from that in a plant cell?   (2 marks)

Ribosomes are found in both eukaryotes and prokaryotes.

(c) What is the function of ribosomes?   (1 mark)

(d) Name one feature that is shown in the diagram that would also be found in a virus. Name a feature that is found in viruses but is not found in prokaryotes or eukaryotes.   (2 marks)

ℯ This question is all about prokaryotes and viruses. Students often neglect this area of the cell structure/organisation topic and instead just focus on animal and plant cells. Make sure you have a good understanding of this area — focus especially on comparisons between eukaryotes and prokaryotes.

Student A

(a) Has a cell wall, DNA and a flagellum.

ℯ **0/3 marks awarded** This answer scores none of the 3 marks available because none of the features listed is specific to prokaryotes. Cell walls are also found in plant cells, DNA is found in all cells and flagella are found in a number of non-prokaryote cells such as sperm.

(b) A prokaryotic cell wall is made of murein and a plant cell wall is made from cellulose.

ℯ **2/2 marks awarded** This is a good answer that gains both marks.

(c) Protein synthesis

e **1/1 mark awarded** Protein synthesis is the correct function for ribosomes, so this answer gains the mark available.

(d) Viruses could have DNA, which is shown in the diagram, and a capsule, which eukaryotes and prokaryotes do not.

e **1/2 marks awarded** Student A has made a common mistake here and misses 1 of the 2 marks available. Viruses have capsids whereas prokaryotes have capsules. DNA is found in both prokaryotes and some viruses though, so this comparison scores 1 mark.

Student B

(a) The cell shown is a prokaryotic cell as it has no membrane-bound organelles such as mitochondria, its DNA is free in the cytoplasm and it has a mesosome.

e **3/3 marks awarded** This is a good, detailed answer that identifies three key prokaryote features shown in the diagram. It gains the full 3 marks.

(b) The prokaryote cell wall is not made of cellulose.

e **1/2 marks awarded** This answer is correct, but as the question is worth 2 marks more detail is required. Always look carefully at the mark allocation for questions and ensure that you make at least as many separate points as there are marks. The second mark would be awarded for giving murein as the chemical that prokaryote cell walls are made from.

(c) Protein synthesis

e **1/1 mark awarded** This is the correct answer and scores the 1 mark available.

(d) Viruses have a protein coat and eukaryotes and prokaryotes do not. Viruses could have DNA, which is shown in the diagram.

e **2/2 marks awarded** This is a correct answer and scores both the available marks. Capsid instead of protein coat would also have been accepted.

Question 5

The photo shows an electron micrograph of a eukaryotic cell.

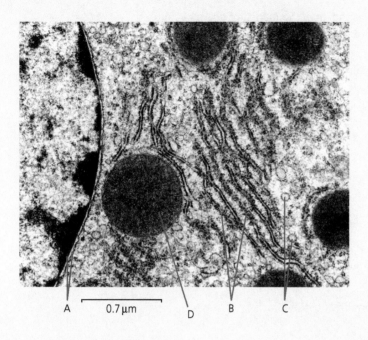

(a) Name the features A, B and C. (3 marks)

(b) Feature A has pores along its length. Explain the function of these pores. (1 mark)

(c) Feature D is a mitochondrion. Give three ways in which the structure of this organelle is similar to that of a chloroplast. (3 marks)

(d) Calculate the magnification of this electron micrograph. (2 marks)

ⓔ Students often find questions with electron micrographs challenging. It is important to remember that you will have learned about all the features you will be asked to identify. If the feature does not look immediately familiar, try to think about the key features of organelles: what general shapes are they, do they have internal structures etc.? Calculating magnification is another of the required mathematical skills, so make sure you can apply the magnification formula and rearrange it.

Student A

(a) A = nuclear membrane, B = smooth endoplasmic reticulum, C = vesicles

ⓔ **2/3 marks awarded** Student A has correctly identified features A and C, but feature B is rough endoplasmic reticulum not smooth endoplasmic reticulum. The distinguishing feature is the dots that can be seen on the endoplasmic reticulum in the image. These are ribosomes and are found on rough endoplasmic reticulum. Student A therefore scores 2 out of the 3 marks available.

(b) They allow things to leave the nucleus.

ⓔ **0/1 mark awarded** This answer lacks sufficient detail to get the mark. The student should have stated what things leave the nucleus, such as mRNA.

(c) A chloroplast also has a double membrane, its own ribosomes and is used in respiration like a mitochondrion.

ⓔ **2/3 marks awarded** This answer gains 2 marks for the first two points. However, the last point is not only wrong (chloroplasts carry out photosynthesis, not respiration), but the question asked for structural similarities. What the organelle *does* is a functional feature, not a structural feature.

(d) 2200/0.7 = 3143×

ⓔ **0/2 marks awarded** Student A has failed to correctly convert the actual diameter of the mitochondrion in the electron micrograph from cm into μm (they have missed off a zero) and therefore the calculation is incorrect.

Student B

(a) A = nuclear membrane, B = RER, C = vesicles

ⓔ **2/3 marks awarded** Student B has correctly identified features A and C, but loses the mark for feature B for abbreviating rough endoplasmic reticulum to RER. With the exception of abbreviations of biochemicals such as DNA, RNA and ATP, you should avoid abbreviations in exam answers.

(b) They allow mRNA to pass out of the nucleus into the cytoplasm.

ⓔ **1/1 mark awarded** This is an excellent answer that gains the mark.

(c) Like a mitochondrion, a chloroplast has a double membrane, its own DNA and folded internal membranes that give a large surface area.

ⓔ **3/3 marks awarded** This is a detailed, well-explained answer that gets all 3 marks.

(d) 2.2 cm actual diameter of mitochondrion = 22 000 μm

22 000/0.7 = 31 429 times magnification

ⓔ **2/2 marks awarded** Student B has correctly converted the actual diameter of the mitochondrion from cm to μm and then correctly applied the formula to give the correct answer, scoring both available marks.

Cell membranes and transport

Question 6

The diagram shows a section of the plasma membrane.

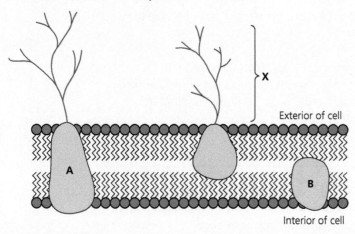

(a) (i) Distinguish between:

   features A and B

   features X and B (2 marks)

   (ii) Give a possible function for feature X. (1 mark)

The table shows the rate of uptake of different molecules and ions into an animal cell.

Molecule	Rate of uptake into the cell/ arbitrary units
Glucose	50
Na$^+$	10
Oxygen	1500
Carbon dioxide	900

(b) (i) How would the movement of glucose through the plasma membrane differ from the movement of oxygen through the plasma membrane? Explain this difference. (4 marks)

   (ii) Further investigation showed that nitrates were entering the cell against the concentration gradient. Explain how this is possible. (2 marks)

@ This question is all about comparisons. Think carefully about each aspect of the question and try to find the key differences. Ensure that your answers contain both sides of the comparison.

Student A

(a) (i) Feature A is an intrinsic protein whereas feature B is an extrinsic protein. Feature X is part of a glycoprotein and feature B is not.

e **1/2 marks awarded** The first comparison is correct and scores 1 mark. The second comparison does not score the other available mark — feature X is a specific part of a glycoprotein (the carbohydrate chain) and Student A does not score a mark for simply saying 'feature B is not'.

> **(ii)** Cell-to-cell recognition.

e **1/1 mark awarded** This is the correct answer and scores the mark available. 'Used in cell-to-cell signalling' would also have been accepted.

> **(b) (i)** Glucose is a large, polar molecule, so it moves through the membrane by facilitated diffusion. This is through a carrier protein and requires energy in the form of ATP. Oxygen is a small, non-polar molecule, so it can diffuse through the phospholipid bilayer.

e **3/4 marks awarded** Student A scores 3 of the 4 available marks for this question. They have correctly identified that glucose moves through the plasma membrane by facilitated diffusion using a carrier protein, but they then state that ATP is involved. This is incorrect and negates the mark that would have been awarded for explaining how glucose moves through the plasma membrane. It is an important point to remember that in the short-answer sections of the paper, an incorrect statement among correct statements will cause you to lose a mark.

> **(ii)** Nitrates are entering the cell by active transport.

e **1/2 marks awarded** This answer is correct, but it only scores 1 out of the 2 marks available as Student A has not explained how active transport can occur against the concentration gradient (by using ATP and a carrier protein as a pump).

Student B

> **(a) (i)** Feature A is an intrinsic protein and feature B is an extrinsic protein. Feature X is a carbohydrate and feature B is a protein.

e **2/2 marks awarded** This is a good comparison that scores both marks.

> **(ii)** Cell-to-cell signalling.

e **1/1 mark awarded** This is the correct answer and gets 1 mark.

> **(b) (i)** Glucose would move through the membrane by facilitated diffusion. Oxygen can diffuse through the phospholipid bilayer as it is a small, lipid-soluble molecule.

ⓔ **3/4 marks awarded** Everything Student B has written for this answer is correct, but they have failed to explain why glucose has to move through the plasma membrane by facilitated diffusion (it is due to it being a large, polar molecule), so only scores 3 of the 4 marks available.

> **(ii)** As nitrates are entering the cell against the concentration gradient, active transport must be occurring. Active transport requires ATP and a carrier protein to act as a pump.

ⓔ **2/2 marks awarded** This is a well-explained answer that scores both available marks.

Question 7

The graph shows the effect of lipid solubility on the rate of diffusion of molecules through a plasma membrane at two temperatures, 20°C and 50°C.

(a) Describe and explain the effect of lipid solubility of a molecule on the rate of diffusion through a cell membrane at 20°C. (2 marks)

(b) Describe and explain the difference between the results at 20°C and 50°C in terms of plasma membrane fluidity. (2 marks)

(c) The presence of which molecule in the plasma membrane reduces the fluidity of the plasma membrane? (1 mark)

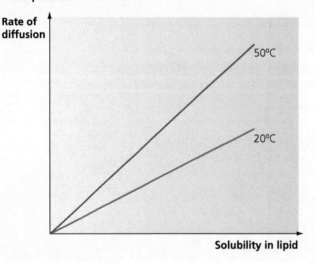

ⓔ Scoring highly on this question depends entirely on fully understanding the graph. Take time to study it carefully and don't rush into answering the questions. Parts (a) and (b) both ask you to describe and explain. The fact that the question asks you to describe as well as explain means that there will be marks available for just describing the trend of the graph. Even without a full understanding of the scientific theory, it should be possible for all students to score some of the marks in this question. This illustrates the importance of not becoming disheartened with a question you are having difficulty understanding — there may still be some marks you can get. This question is a particularly good example of this as part (c) is just factual recall.

Student A

(a) When the solubility of the molecule in lipids increases, it is able to move through the phospholipid bilayer of the plasma membrane much more easily.

e **1/2 marks awarded** This answer scores 1 out of the 2 marks available. Student A has identified the link between lipid solubility and ability to pass through the phospholipids, but has failed to answer the 'describe' part of the question. A simple statement saying that as the solubility in lipids increases, the rate of diffusion through the plasma membrane increases would have scored the other mark. This is a classic example of a student answering the hard part of the question and assuming that in doing so they would also get the mark for the simpler 'describe' section. It is vital that you clearly state the answers to all questions. In this case, it is clear to the examiner that the student knows what the graph shows, but unless the student states it the examiner cannot award the mark.

(b) At 20°C the rate of diffusion is much less than at 50°C at all lipid solubilities. This is due to the diffusing molecules having a greater kinetic energy and therefore passing through the phospholipid bilayer much more easily.

e **0/2 marks awarded** This statement is correct but it scores neither of the 2 marks available. An increase in temperature increases the kinetic energy of the diffusing molecules and so leads to a greater rate of diffusion, but the question specifically asks students to explain the difference in terms of the membrane's fluidity. It is a common mistake for students to answer the question they wish to answer instead of the question that is asked. If the question specifically states that the answer should relate to the fluidity of the membrane, an answer that does not mention membrane fluidity will not get the marks.

(c) Cholesterol.

e **1/1 marks awarded** This is the correct answer and gains 1 mark.

Student B

(a) As the solubility in lipid increases, the rate of diffusion also increases. This is because molecules that are lipid-soluble are able to pass through the phospholipid bilayer of the plasma membrane more easily.

e **2/2 marks awarded** This is an excellent answer that concisely describes and explains the trend of the graph and so scores both available marks.

(b) At 50°C the components of the plasma membrane have more kinetic energy so they move more, causing the membrane to become more fluid. A more fluid membrane means that the molecules can pass through the phospholipid bilayer more easily, leading to the greater rate of diffusion at 50°C when compared to 20°C.

ℯ **2/2 marks awarded** This answer relates the difference between rates of diffusion at 20°C and 50°C to the increased fluidity of the membrane and explains that this is because of an increase in kinetic energy of the components of the plasma membrane. Both marks are given.

(c) Cholesterol.

ℯ **1/1 mark awarded** This answer is correct and scores the 1 mark available.

Question 8

The graph shows the change in mass of potato cylinders in different external solute potentials.

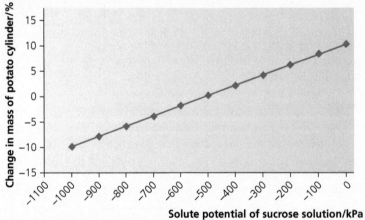

(a) (i) Explain the importance of using % change in mass in this investigation as opposed to change of mass in grams. (1 mark)

   (ii) The experiment was repeated using five new samples and the results in the table were obtained. Calculate the % change in mass for each of the five samples. (2 marks)

Sample	Initial mass/g	Final mass/g
A	1.73	1.62
B	2.07	1.87
C	1.85	1.75
D	2.11	2.20
E	2.01	2.17

(iii) Using the graph, estimate the solute potentials that produced these changes in mass. (2 marks)

The diagram shows the water potential of three plant cells.

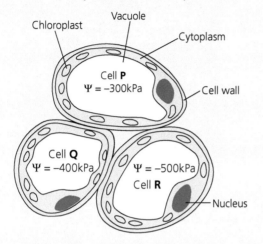

(b) Draw arrows on the diagram to show the movement of water between cells. (2 marks)

The photo shows plant cells that have been put in two different concentrations of sucrose solutions, P and Q.

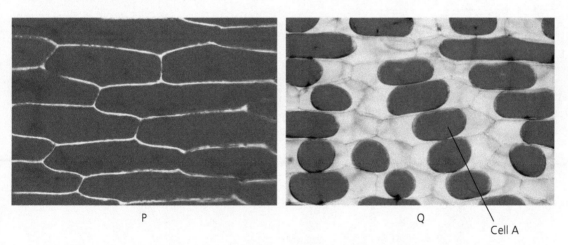

P   Q

Cell A

(c) (i) Which of the solutions has the highest concentration of sucrose? Explain your answer. (2 marks)

(ii) The solute potential of the cells in solution Q is −200 kPa. What is the water potential of cell A? Explain how you arrived at your answer. (4 marks)

ⓔ It is easy to make mistakes in water potential questions, so don't rush into an answer. Go through each part of the question methodically and always check back on the work you have done. Question (c) (ii) is particularly challenging. If you get to a question like this, remember that the answer must be based on something in the specification, take a bit of time to think around the question and see if you can work out how it relates to what you know.

Student A

(a) (i) Not all the potato samples had the same starting mass. Therefore, in order to compare the changes in mass, the % change in mass must be calculated.

e **1/1 mark awarded** This is the correct answer and gains the 1 mark available.

(ii)

Sample	% change in mass
A	−6.36
B	−9.66
C	−5.41
D	96
E	7.96

e **1/2 marks awarded** Student A has incorrectly calculated the change in mass for sample D. This should have been obvious as the value is so much greater than all the rest.

(iii)

Sample	Solute potential/kPa
A	−800
B	0
C	−750
D	Greater than 0
E	−100

e **1/2 marks awarded** Student A has given an incorrect value for the solute potential for sample D. Again, this should have been obvious as such a change would be caused by a solute potential greater than 0, which is impossible.

(b)

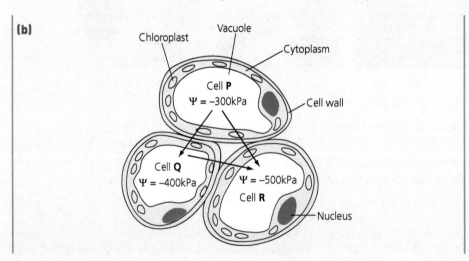

ⓔ **2/2 marks awarded** The direction of movement of the water is correctly shown, going from a higher (less negative) water potential to a lower (more negative) water potential and gets 2 marks.

> **(c) (i)** Solution Q has the highest concentration of sucrose of the two solutions. You can tell from the appearance of the cells.

ⓔ **1/2 marks awarded** Student A has correctly identified that solution Q has the highest concentration of sucrose. However, they have failed to explain why, so only score 1 mark.

> **(ii)** The water potential of the cell is 0 kPa as the cells are plasmolysed.

ⓔ **1/4 marks awarded** Student A clearly does not know how to answer this question. However, the student still scores 1 mark by using the key word 'plasmolysed'. This shows how it is possible to pick up marks even in complex questions by using appropriate key words.

Student B

(a) (i) The potato samples did not all start with the same mass. Therefore, in order to make a fair comparison of the changes in mass, the % change in mass must be calculated for each sample.

ⓔ **1/1 mark awarded** This is the correct answer and scores the mark.

(ii)

Sample	% change in mass
A	−6.36
B	−9.66
C	−5.41
D	4.27
E	7.96

ⓔ **2/2 marks awarded** Student B scores both available marks here as all the answers are correct.

(iii)

Sample	Solute potential/kPa
A	−800
B	0
C	−750
D	−300
E	−100

ⓔ **2/2 marks awarded** Student B scores both the marks as all the answers are correct. When asked to estimate in a question, there will often be a margin of error given.

(b)

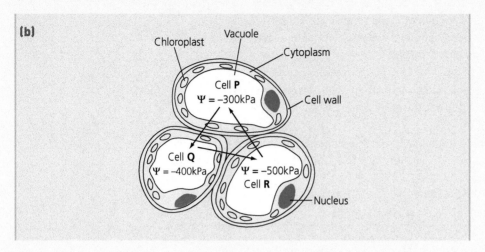

ⓔ **1/2 marks awarded** One of the arrows is pointing in the wrong direction, so Student B loses one of the available marks and scores only 1 mark. This incorrect answer to a simple question by an able student highlights the importance of checking answers involving water potential. The use of negative numbers can make it easy to make errors.

(c) (i) Solution Q has the highest concentration of the two solutions as the cells in solution Q are plasmolysed. Therefore, water must have left the cell by osmosis, from a high to a low water potential.

ⓔ **2/2 marks awarded** This is a detailed answer that scores both available marks. It would also be possible to score marks by explaining why solution P does not have the highest concentration of sucrose — the water potential of this solution must be high as water moves into the cell so it is turgid.

(ii) The water potential of the cell is −200 kPa. This is the same as the solute potential. As the cell is plasmolysed, the pressure potential is zero. This is because the cytoplasm is not pushing against the cell wall.

ⓔ **4/4 marks awarded** Student B has correctly realised that as the cell is plasmolysed there is no pressure potential, so the solute potential is equal to the water potential. The student therefore scores all 4 of the available marks.

Biological reactions are regulated by enzymes

Question 9

The graph shows the mass of product formed by an enzyme-controlled reaction over time.

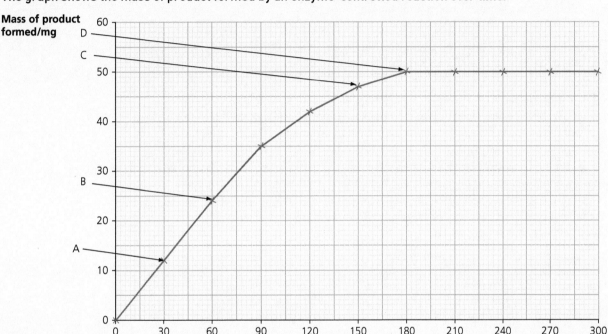

(a) Calculate and derive the units for the rate of reaction between:
   points A and B
   points C and D   (2 marks)

(b) Explain why these two values are different.   (3 marks)

(c) Explain the shape of the curve after point D.   (2 marks)

ⓔ Questions asking you to calculate rate are quite common in exams. It is an easy calculation — the rate is found by dividing the mass of product by the time taken to produce it. The units will be whatever the product or substrate is measured in over the unit of time. The rest of the question is fairly straightforward. The main issue with a product over time graph like this one is that students often mix up this graph with the rate of reaction/substrate concentration graph.

Student A

(a) Points A and B: 12/30 = 0.4 mg min⁻¹

   Points C and D: 3/30 = 0.1 mg min⁻¹

Questions & Answers

ⓔ 2/2 marks awarded The calculations and units are correct for 2 marks.

(b) The rate of reaction was faster at A–B than at C–D. This is because C–D is closer to the maximum rate of reaction.

ⓔ 0/3 marks awarded Student A has failed to understand that this graph shows a reaction occurring over time, so incorrectly believes the levelling out of the graph represents a maximum rate of reaction.

(c) After point D, all the active sites are full all the time. This means the reaction has reached its maximum rate.

ⓔ 0/2 marks awarded Student A's answer reflects what can happen if you fail to identify the type of graph you are being asked to look at. This student clearly learned the shapes of the different rate of reaction graphs and the facts that accompany them (the graph levels out due to all the active sites being full all the time) and then has just reeled if off here. This single mistake has led to Student A scoring only 2 marks out of a possible 7 and underlines the necessity of not just learning the specification content by heart but really thinking about it and trying to understand it. The only marks this student scored were for the correct rate calculations and units in part (a).

Student B

(a) Points A and B: $12/30 = 0.4\,mg\,min^{-1}$

Points C and D: $3/30 = 0.1\,mg\,min^{-1}$

ⓔ 2/2 marks awarded Both rates are calculated correctly and the correct units are given, so this answer gets 2 marks.

(b) The rate of reaction was fastest at A–B as at this point there was a large concentration of substrate so the enzyme concentration was the limiting factor. At C–D the rate of reaction is slower. This is because the concentration of substrate has decreased as it has been converted into products. This means there is a reduced chance of a collision between an active site and a substrate molecule therefore less product is produced per minute.

ⓔ 3/3 marks awarded This is an excellent answer that scores all 3 marks available. There was 1 mark for explaining that A–B was faster because there is a large concentration of substrate at this point, near the start of the reaction. Student B scored the other 2 marks by identifying that the C–D rate of reaction is slower because some of the substrate has been converted to product so there is less chance of a successful collision between a substrate molecule and an active site.

(c) After point D, the graph is flat. This means the rate of reaction is 0 as all the substrate has been converted into product.

(e) **2/2 marks awarded** Student B scores both marks by saying that the rate of reaction is zero because all the substrates have been converted into product.

Student B's answer illustrates the difference that good understanding and preparation for exams can make. This student has obviously thought carefully about what the graph shows and was able to score all the marks available for this question.

Question 10

The graph shows the rate of reaction of the enzyme lactase at different pHs, when it is immobilised and when it is free in solution.

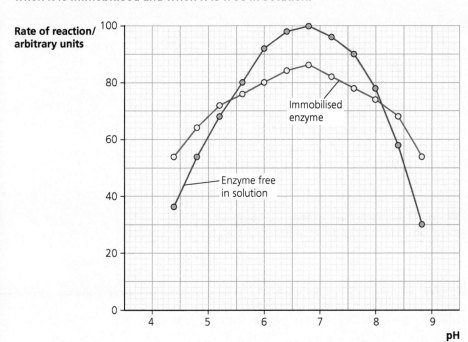

(a) Lactase hydrolyses the glycosidic bond in lactose. What are the products of this reaction? (2 marks)

(b) Explain the rate of reaction of lactase free in solution at:
pH 6.8
pH 4.5 (3 marks)

(c) Using information from the graph, describe two effects of immobilisation on the rate of reaction of lactase. (2 marks)

ⓔ It is important in questions involving graphs to study them carefully. You are looking for what the graph is showing you (this will be the answer to 'describe' questions) and the underlying theory that explains the shape of the curve (this will answer an 'explain' question). Part (c) asks you to use information from the graph, so make sure you do this and don't bring in other additional information that might not be relevant.

Student A

(a) Glucose and fructose.

ⓔ **1/2 marks awarded** Student A scores only 1 mark as they have failed to identify galactose as the monosaccharide that bonds with glucose to form the disaccharide lactose.

(b) pH 6.8 — this is the enzyme's optimum pH, so at this point the rate of reaction is the fastest.

pH 4.5 — the rate of reaction is low as the enzymes are becoming denatured.

ⓔ **2/3 marks awarded** For the first point, Student A has given a good answer and scores the mark available. However, for the second part of the question the student scores only 1 of the 2 marks available. They have used the term 'denatured', which scores 1 mark, but have failed to explain what it means. In a question like this, you should always explain key terms.

(c) At the optimum pH, the immobilised enzyme has a lower rate of reaction than the non-immobilised enzyme. The immobilised enzymes survive better at extreme pHs.

ⓔ **1/2 marks awarded** The first part of this answer is correct, but the second part lacks detail and uses the term 'survives', so Student A gets only 1 of the 2 marks available. The use of 'survive' illustrates a common mistake that students make when answering enzyme questions. Words such as 'live', 'kill' and 'survive' are often used in answers. These imply that an enzyme is alive and such terms should not be used in exam question answers —enzymes are not living, they are just chemicals.

Student B

(a) Glucose and galactose.

ⓔ **2/2 marks awarded** These are the two correct monosaccharides that make up lactose, so score 2 marks.

(b) pH 6.8 — this is the enzyme's optimum pH, so at this point the rate of reaction is the fastest.

pH 4.5 — at this pH, the lactase enzymes are denatured. This pH has caused a change in the tertiary structure of the active site so the substrates can no longer bind so the rate of reaction has decreased.

e 3/3 marks awarded This is an excellent answer to this question — the second part is very detailed but it is better to write too full an answer than too little and it is always worth explaining what 'denaturing' means.

(c) The maximum rate of reaction of the immobilised lactase is lower than the free lactase. However, at a pH above 8.1 the immobilised lactase has a higher rate of reaction than the free lactase.

e 2/2 marks awarded Both of these differences are correct and this answer scores 2 marks. It would also have been possible to score marks for stating that the rate of reaction of the immobilised enzyme is higher at pHs below 5.8.

◼ Nucleic acids and their function

Question 11

(a) Why can DNA be described as a polymer? (2 marks)

(b) Explain three ways in which mRNA differs from DNA. (3 marks)

(c) The nitrogenous bases in a sample of DNA were analysed. Thymine was found to make up 13% of the nitrogenous bases. Calculate the percentage of cytosine in the sample. Explain how you arrived at your answer. (3 marks)

e This question requires mainly factual recall and a fairly simple calculation so should not prove too difficult.

Student A

(a) It is made up of monomers.

e 1/2 marks awarded This answer is correct, but a single point like this will only score 1 mark.

(b) DNA has thymine nitrogenous base, mRNA has uracil. DNA nucleotides have deoxyribose, mRNA nucleotides have ribose. mRNA is single-stranded, DNA is double-stranded.

e 3/3 marks awarded This is an excellent answer — it makes three good comparisons so scores all 3 marks available.

(c) 13% of thymine means there must be 13% cytosine.

ⓔ **0/3 marks awarded** Student A has mixed up the complementary base pairs and believes thymine pairs with cytosine. This means this answer scores no marks. The student could have picked up this error when checking through the exam paper by looking at the mark allocation for this question. If the answer to this question were so simple it would not be worth 3 marks. Student A has also not explained how they arrived at this answer. The term 'complementary base pairing' was needed to get a mark.

Student B

(a) It is made up of many monomers known as nucleotides.

ⓔ **2/2 marks awarded** This is a detailed answer that scores 2 marks.

(b) mRNA contains the nitrogenous base uracil, whereas DNA contains the nitrogenous base thymine. DNA has a different pentose sugar to mRNA and it is double-stranded.

ⓔ **1/3 marks awarded** The first point is a good comparison and scores 1 mark. The next two points are both correct, but as they are not comparative statements they score no marks.

(c) There is complementary base pairing between adenine and thymine and cytosine and guanine. So, the amount of thymine = the amount of adenine = 13 + 13 = 26%. Therefore, 100 – 26 = 74% amount of cytosine and guanine. As the amount of cytosine = the amount of guanine, the % of cytosine = 74/2 = 37%.

ⓔ **3/3 marks awarded** This excellent answer scores all 3 marks. First, Student B has stated the fundamental concept behind answering a question like this. As there is complementary base pairing, the proportions of the rest of the bases can be calculated from the amount of one base, as has been shown in this student's answer.

Question 12

(a) In what stage of the cell cycle does DNA replication occur? (1 mark)

Meselson and Stahl's investigation into DNA replication relied on DNA nucleotides containing different isotopes of nitrogen ^{14}N and ^{15}N.

(b) Which part of the DNA nucleotide contains the ^{14}N or the ^{15}N? (1 mark)

Meselson and Stahl cultured bacteria in a medium containing ^{14}N. After cell lysis and centrifugation, the DNA was in the position shown in the first tube below. They then transferred the bacteria to a medium containing ^{15}N. After each division of bacteria, they centrifuged DNA sampled from some of the cells.

(c) (i) Complete the diagrams to show the positions of DNA in the tubes for the second and third generations. (3 marks)

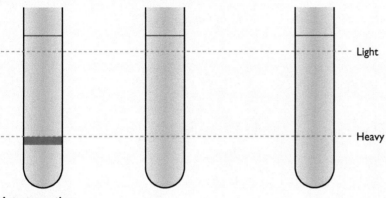

1st generation

(ii) Explain how this provided evidence of semi-conservative replication. (2 marks)

e Most of the marks in this question are related to Meselson and Stahl's investigation into DNA replication. Make sure that you understand this experiment fully and can recall the results as well as explain what they show.

Student A

(a) In prophase of mitosis.

e **0/1 mark awarded** Student A has made a common mistake in thinking that DNA replication occurs in mitosis. DNA replication is important in both mitosis and meiosis, so it occurs during interphase.

(b) The nitrogenous base.

e **1/1 mark awarded** This is a correct answer and scores 1 mark.

(c) (i)

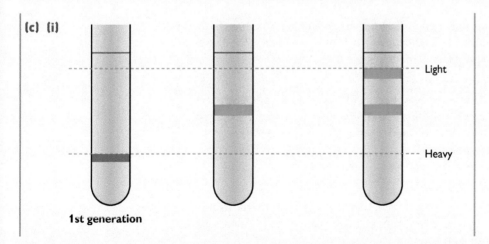

1st generation

e **3/3 marks awarded** The student has drawn the correct bands in both tubes, so scores all available marks.

(ii) It shows that each new DNA molecule contains newly synthesised DNA.

ⓔ **0/2 marks awarded** This answer is far too simple to score either of the marks available.

Student B

(a) Interphase.

ⓔ **1/1 mark awarded** This is a correct answer and scores the 1 mark available.

(b) In adenine.

ⓔ **0/1 mark awarded** This answer is actually too specific. Adenine is a nitrogenous base so it would indeed contain the ^{14}N or ^{15}N, but so would all the other nitrogenous bases.

(c) (i)

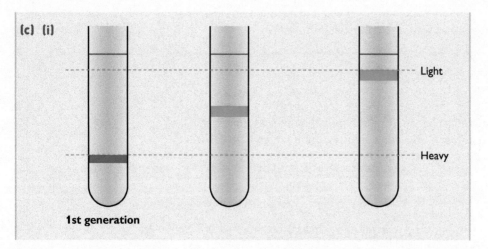

Light

Heavy

1st generation

ⓔ **2/3 marks awarded** The student has drawn only two bands on the tubes. As this is a 3-mark question, the question is guiding you to draw three bands. The two drawn are correct, but the missing third band means Student B cannot get the third mark.

(ii) This investigation provides evidence that DNA is semi-conservatively replicated as it shows that each DNA molecule contains one original strand and one newly synthesised strand. This is shown by the continued presence of the ^{15}N strand (forming the hybrid $^{15}N/^{14}N$ strand) and the formation of a ^{14}N strand in the third generation.

ⓔ **2/2 marks awarded** This is a fantastic answer that scores both marks available, one for describing what semi-conservative replication is (one original and one newly formed strand) and one for relating the results to this (the continued presence of the ^{15}N strand and the formation of a DNA molecule just containing ^{14}N).

Question 13

The following is a sequence of mRNA:

CUAGAGGGG

(a) Write out the DNA strand that this mRNA strand was produced from. (1 mark)

(b) Which enzyme would produce this mRNA strand? (1 mark)

(c) Using the codon table shown, determine the sequence of amino acids that this strand of mRNA codes for. (1 mark)

Two separate mutations in the same sequence of DNA resulted in the transcription of the mRNA sequences, A and B, as shown.

Mutation A: AUCGAGGGG

Mutation B: CUAGAGGGA

(d) Using the codon table, explain why mutation A might have much more serious consequences than mutation B. (4 marks)

Second position

		U	C	A	G	
First position (5' end)	**U**	UUU ⎤ Phe UUC ⎦ UUA ⎤ Leu UUG ⎦	UCU ⎤ UCC ⎥ Ser UCA ⎥ UCG ⎦	UAU ⎤ Tyr UAC ⎦ UAA stop UAG stop	UGU ⎤ Cys UGC ⎦ UGA stop UGG Trp	U C A G	**Third position (3' end)**
	C	CUU ⎤ CUC ⎥ Leu CUA ⎥ CUG ⎦	CCU ⎤ CCC ⎥ Pro CCA ⎥ CCG ⎦	CAU ⎤ His CAC ⎦ CAA ⎤ Gln CAG ⎦	CGU ⎤ CGC ⎥ Arg CGA ⎥ CGG ⎦	U C A G	
	A	AUU ⎤ Ile AUC ⎥ AUA ⎦ AUG Met	ACU ⎤ ACC ⎥ Thr ACA ⎥ ACG ⎦	AAU ⎤ Asn AAC ⎦ AAA ⎤ Lys AAG ⎦	AGU ⎤ Ser AGC ⎦ AGA ⎤ Arg AGG ⎦	U C A G	
	G	GUU ⎤ GUC ⎥ Val GUA ⎥ GUG ⎦	GCU ⎤ GCC ⎥ Ala GCA ⎥ GCG ⎦	GAU ⎤ Asp GAC ⎦ GAA ⎤ Glu GAG ⎦	GGU ⎤ GGC ⎥ Gly GGA ⎥ GGG ⎦	U C A G	

ⓔ This is a fairly straightforward question, but it is nevertheless important in any question that involves genetic codes to be careful when writing your answers and to check them thoroughly. The last part is a 4-mark question, so make sure you answer it in sufficient detail.

Student A

(a) GAUCUCCCC.

e **0/1 mark awarded** Student A has made a common mistake and correctly written down the complementary sequence, but they have failed to replace U (uracil) with T (thymine). Remember that in mRNA uracil replaces thymine, whereas thymine is found in DNA. This is an example of a simple mistake that has cost the student an easy mark, and underlines that it is so important to check back over your answers to avoid mistakes like this.

(b) RNA polymerase.

e **1/1 mark awarded** This is the correct answer and scores 1 mark.

(c) Leucine, glutamic acid, serine.

e **0/1 mark awarded** Again, the student has made a simple mistake that has cost them what should have been an easy mark.

(d) Mutation A appears to be a much more serious mutation than B. It could lead to the incorrect formation of the polypeptide as the primary sequence of the polypeptide (the sequence of the amino acids) will be different. This could lead to the protein being non-functional.

e **3/4 marks awarded** This is a good answer, although the first sentence repeats information given in the question and so is unnecessary. The student has clearly not realised why mutation A is a more serious mutation than mutation A, but they have written a detailed explanation of the possible consequences of DNA mutation and that has scored them 3 of the 4 marks available. The fourth mark was for saying that mutation B is less serious as the same amino acid (glycine) will still be coded for by the last codon (GGG and GGA both code for glycine).

Student B

(a) GATCTCCCC.

e **1/1 mark awarded** This the correct DNA sequence so this answer scores the 1 mark available.

(b) RNA polymerase.

e **1/1 mark awarded** This is correct for 1 mark.

(c) Leucine, glutamic acid and glycine.

ⓔ **1/1 mark awarded** This is the correct sequence of amino acids, so scores the 1 mark available.

(d) As the mutation is a substitution mutation, the replacement of the final G in the last codon with A means that glycine is still coded for, so the correct amino acid is still produced.

ⓔ **1/4 marks awarded** The student has fully understood the idea behind this question, but they have not developed their answer so did not score all of the 4 marks available. The student only scores 1 mark for correctly stating that mutation B is less serious as the correct amino acid is still produced, but they have not described why mutation A is so much more potentially serious. Because the incorrect amino acid is produced, the polypeptide's primary structure will be altered, which could result in the protein being non-functional. This question illustrates how important it is to look carefully at the mark allocations for each question to ensure that you are putting enough detail into your answers to score all the marks available.

▌Genetic information is passed on to daughter cells

Question 14

(a) In which stages of mitosis do the following events occur?

   (i) The nuclear membrane reforms.   (1 mark)

   (ii) Spindle fibres contract and pull sister chromatids to the opposite poles of the cell.   (1 mark)

   (iii) The nuclear membrane breaks down.   (1 mark)

   (iv) Spindle fibres join to the chromosomes at the centromere.   (1 mark)

(b) A student was observing some plant tissue in which cells were undergoing mitosis. She saw a large number of cells that looked like cell A, but very few that looked like cell B. Identify the stages of mitosis of cell A and cell B and explain the difference in the numbers of cells she saw.   (4 marks)

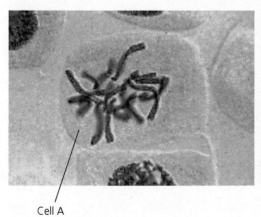

Cell A

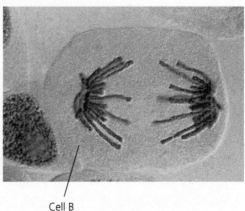

Cell B

Questions & Answers

e Mitosis questions often ask you to match up what is happening in a phase with its correct name. It is therefore important to have a firm grasp of exactly what occurs in each stage. This question also involves looking at photos of real plant cells undergoing mitosis. Students often find this challenging because they don't always look like the diagrams we usually look at. In a cell division photo, the key things are the chromosomes (the red-brown squiggles here) — look at how they are behaving and relate that to what you know the chromosomes do at each stage of mitosis.

Student A

(a) (i) Telophase.

(ii) Metaphase.

(iii) Prophase.

(iv) Anaphase.

---

e **2/4 marks awarded** Student A only scores 2 of the 4 marks available (for parts (i) and (iii)) as they have mixed up anaphase (the correct answer for part (ii)) and metaphase (the correct answer for part (iv)). It is important to be clear in your mind about what occurs in each stage.

(b) Cell A is in prophase and cell B is in metaphase. Prophase is a much longer phase than metaphase so you would expect to see more cells in prophase in a sample.

e **2/4 marks awarded** Mixing up metaphase and anaphase again loses the student marks here. The chromosomes separate and are pulled to the opposite poles of the cell during anaphase. Student A picks up 2 marks for correctly stating that cell A is in prophase and that prophase is a longer phase so you would expect to see a large number of cells in this stage.

Student B

(a) (i) Telophase.

(ii) Anaphase.

(iii) Prophase.

(iv) Metaphase.

---

e **4/4 marks awarded** All four of these stages are correct, so Student B scores all 4 available marks.

(b) Cell A is in prophase whereas cell B is in anaphase. Prophase is a very long phase, so more of the cells at this point in time are in prophase.

ⓔ **3/4 marks awarded** Student B has correctly identified both stages and has stated that prophase is a long phase and therefore more of the cells would be in prophase at any one time. However, this student does not score the fourth mark available for this question as they have not made a comparison with cell B to say that anaphase is a much quicker phase so you would expect to see only a small number of cells in anaphase at any one time.

Question 15

The graph shows the change in the amount of DNA during a cell cycle.

(a) Identify stage A. (1 mark)

(b) Explain the change in DNA during stage A. (1 mark)

(c) Name two other processes that occur during stage A. (2 marks)

(d) Explain the change in DNA during stage D. (2 marks)

(e) How does mitosis make sure that an identical cell line is produced and ensure genetic stability? (1 mark)

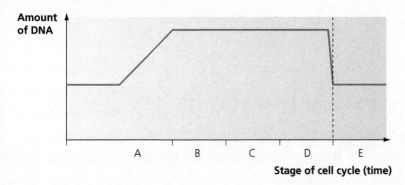

ⓔ The questions involving this graph are quite challenging. It is vital to ensure that you work out what a graph is showing before starting to write your answer, as a single misunderstanding can result in the loss of a large number of marks.

Student A

(a) Stage A is interphase.

ⓔ **1/1 mark awarded** Student A has correctly identified interphase and gains the mark.

(b) DNA replication has occurred so the amount of DNA has doubled.

ⓔ **1/1 mark awarded** Student A has correctly identified the DNA doubling because of DNA replication and so gains the mark.

(c) ATP is produced and protein synthesis occurs.

ⓔ **2/2 marks awarded** Both of these processes occur in interphase, so this answer gets both marks.

(d) The amount of DNA halves as each daughter cell receives one copy.

ⓔ **1/2 marks awarded** This answer can only get 1 mark as it makes only one point (that each daughter cell receives a copy of the DNA). The second mark would be awarded for stating that cytokinesis occurs, splitting the cell into two daughter cells. Try to use key words whenever possible because there are often marks available for their correct use.

(e) Mitosis ensures that the daughter cells are exactly the same in every way to the parent cell.

ⓔ **0/1 mark awarded** This is another example of an answer that, although it is correct, does not contain enough detail to be awarded a mark. The key point here is that mitosis produces daughter cells that are genetically identical to the parent cell. This is important because it ensures genetic stability.

Student B

(a) Stage A is showing interphase.

ⓔ **1/1 mark awarded** This is a good answer that scores the mark.

(b) The amount of DNA in the cell has doubled as the DNA has replicated.

ⓔ **1/1 mark awarded** Another good answer for the mark.

(c) New organelles are produced and proteins are synthesised.

ⓔ **2/2 marks awarded** This is correct and scores both the marks.

(d) Cytokinesis has occurred at the end of mitosis. This produces two daughter cells, each of which receives one copy of the DNA. This is shown on the graph by the amount of DNA halving.

ⓔ **2/2 marks awarded** This is a very detailed, well-developed answer that gains both marks.

(e) Each daughter cell is genetically identical to the parent cell.

ⓔ **1/1 mark awarded** Using the key term 'genetically identical' ensures the student gets the mark for this part.

■Extended response question

Question 16

The table shows the latent heat of evaporation and the specific heat capacity of four different substances.

Substance	Latent heat of evaporation/kJ kg^{-1}	Specific heat capacity/J g^{-1} K^{-1}
Ethanol	855	2.440
Ammonia	1369	4.700
Lead	23	0.129
Water	2260	4.180

Explain the values given for water and their biological importance.　　　　　(9 marks)

ⓔ As the extended response question is marked in bands, it is vital that you ensure your answer gets into the highest band possible and that you don't slip down into the lower bands. The generic band descriptors are as follows and these apply to all extended response questions:

7–9 marks The candidate constructs an articulate, integrated account, which shows sequential reasoning. The answer fully addresses the question with no irrelevant inclusions or significant omissions. The candidate uses scientific conventions and vocabulary appropriately and accurately.

4–6 marks The candidate constructs an account correctly linking some relevant points, such as those in the indicative content, showing some reasoning. The answer addresses the question with some omissions. The candidate usually uses scientific conventions and vocabulary appropriately and accurately.

1–3 marks The candidate makes some relevant points, such as those in the indicative content, showing limited reasoning. The answer addresses the question with significant omissions. The candidate has limited use of scientific conventions and vocabulary.

Water is an area of the specification that students often don't spend much time on, but it does come up in the exams and if you have not revised it properly you could lose a lot of marks. When writing an extended response question on something like water, it is important to be specific and to stick to the specification content. For example, writing lots about the physiological effects of dehydration — which is not on the specification — could cost you marks for being irrelevant.

Student A

Water is an important substance for living things. Water has a very high latent heat and a very high specific heat. This is important as the high latent heat means that it takes a large amount of energy to raise the temperature of water by one degree Celsius. This provides a relatively constant internal environment for cells. The high specific heat means a large amount of energy is used to evaporate and evaporation of sweat cools humans down.

A water molecule is made up of an oxygen atom and two hydrogen atoms. Water is a polar molecule as the oxygen atoms have a slight negative charge and the hydrogen atoms have a slight positive charge. Water molecules can form hydrogen bonds between a hydrogen atom and an oxygen atom from two different water molecules. These hydrogen bonds stick the water molecules together and give high surface tension.

It is important that organisms drink enough water. Water is a solvent, which means it dissolves lots of different things. This makes water important in the transport of molecules such as glucose dissolved in blood. Water is also transparent, which allows sharks to hunt their prey.

e **3/9 marks awarded** This answer has fallen into the bottom band. Student A has correctly identified the high values, but then mixed up the meanings of specific heat and latent heat. This is unfortunate because, apart from the mix-up, the student's descriptions of water's high specific heat providing a constant internal environment for cells and the cooling effect caused by the high latent heat are good. They then go on to correctly describe the reasons for the high values, identifying water as a polar molecule, having an uneven distribution of charge and the formation of hydrogen bonds. This is an example of some indicative content showing some limited reasoning. Saying that hydrogen bonds stick the water molecules together rather than use the key word 'cohesion', along with mixing up latent heat and specific heat, means the student has shown limited use of scientific conventions and vocabulary. Student A has then included a large amount of irrelevant information on water's other properties and importance. Information such as this, which does not relate to the question, will not be credited and will prevent you scoring the top band marks. It is therefore vital to make sure you are answering the question asked rather than writing down everything you know about a particular topic.

Student B

Water has both a high specific heat capacity and a high latent heat of evaporation. This is because water is a polar molecule as it has an uneven distribution of charge (the hydrogen has a slight positive charge while the oxygen atom has a slight negative charge). This uneven distribution of charge means water forms hydrogen bonds. This leads to cohesion forces between water molecules which require a large amount of energy to break, hence the high values. The high specific heat of water is very important for living organisms. It means that a large amount of energy is required to raise the temperature of water. This means bodies of water provide a relatively stable environment for aquatic animals. As cells are mainly composed of water it also helps cells maintain a relatively stable internal temperature. As water has a high latent heat of evaporation, a relatively large amount of energy is required to turn water from a liquid into a gas. This means that the evaporation of sweat from the skin of organisms during sweating has a cooling effect.

e 9/9 marks awarded This is an excellent answer. Student B's response is articulated and shows sequential reasoning (i.e. the points follow in a logical order). They identify the fact that water's values for latent heat and specific heat are high and then go on to explain that this is due to hydrogen bonding between water molecules. They then go on to explain the biological importance for this clearly, fully answering the question with no significant omissions. Importantly, they also did not include any irrelevant information, just sticking to answering the question rather than writing down all the properties of water. Finally, the answer is well written with accurate and appropriate vocabulary. This answer easily fulfils all the criteria for the top band, so scores the maximum 9 marks available.

Knowledge check answers

Knowledge check answers

1 If a plant does not have enough magnesium, it cannot make the green pigment chlorophyll.
2 It has an uneven distribution of charge — the oxygen atom is slightly negative and the hydrogen atom is slightly positive.
3 Hydrogen bonds form between the oxygen atom of one water molecule and the hydrogen atom of another.
4 It dissolves a large number of different solutes.
5 High specific heat capacity.
6 When the water evaporates, it provides a cooling effect, e.g. in sweating.
7 Two molecules of glucose.
8 If they were not insoluble in water, when the structure they had formed came into contact with water it would dissolve.
9 Glycogen.
10 β-glucose.
11 Hydrogen bonds.
12 Some OH groups of the β monomers are replaced by nitrogen-containing acetylamine groups.
13 Unsaturated fatty acids have carbon–carbon double bonds; saturated fatty acids do not.
14 An ester bond.
15 20.
16 The type, number and sequence of amino acids.
17 α-helix and β-pleated sheet.
18 Haemoglobin.
19 To produce ATP.
20 To provide a large surface area for ATP synthesis.
21 Because it has ribosomes along its length.
22 Chlorophyll.

23 Intrinsic proteins lie across both layers of the phospholipid bilayer. Extrinsic proteins are in one of the layers or on the surface of the membrane.
24 Facilitated diffusion requires a channel or carrier protein; diffusion does not.
25 It becomes plasmolysed.
26 They lower the activation energy of the reaction.
27 Globular proteins.
28 Pepsin is found in the stomach where the pH is low. Amylase is found in slightly alkaline saliva so has a higher optimum pH.
29 All the available enzyme active sites are full all the time.
30 A competitive inhibitor binds to the active site, preventing the substrate from entering. A non-competitive inhibitor binds to an area of an enzyme away from the active site, changing the shape of the active site so the substrate can no longer bind.
31 Adenine and guanine.
32 Pentose sugar (deoxyribose) and phosphate.
33 The nucleus.
34 Each DNA molecule consists of one original strand and one newly synthesised strand.
35 A gene.
36 The nucleus.
37 The anti-sense strand.
38 Through a nuclear pore.
39 Ribosomes.
40 The anticodon.
41 The centromere.
42 27.
43 Chiasmata.
44 Anaphase I.

Index